THE PHANTOM OF ORGANIC EVOLUTION

The Phantom of
Organic Evolution

By

GEORGE McCREADY PRICE, M. A.

Professor of Geology, Union College, Neb.

*Author of "Q. E. D., or New Light on the Doctrine of
Creation," etc.*

NEW YORK   CHICAGO

Fleming H. Revell Company

LONDON   AND   EDINBURGH

New York: 158 Fifth Avenue
Chicago: 17 North Wabash Ave.
London: 21 Paternoster Square
Edinburgh: 75 Princes Street

PREFACE

SOME twenty-five years ago, while the writer was acting as the principal of a small high school in Eastern Canada, he began his serious study of the problem of organic evolution. His introduction to the problem was through the writings of such men as Grant Allen, Edward Clodd, and Samuel Laing,—not a very promising beginning, some of my readers may say. The study soon extended to Herbert Spencer, Huxley, Le Conte, and Haeckel, together with the various other classical exponents of the doctrine as taught during the closing years of the nineteenth century.

In my endeavour to get back to the original sources, or to the elementary facts, a vast amount of Government Reports and other documents had to be gone through; and for a time it really seemed to me that there must be something to the general idea of organic evolution, after all. But in the course of my investigations I came across an example or two of what the geologists now call " deceptive conformity," where strata alleged to be very " young " occur in perfect conformity over wide areas on top of very much " older " beds, the two being lithically identical, so much so that, " were it not for fossil evidence," as the Government geologist expressed it, " one would naturally suppose that a single formation was being dealt with." To me it seemed self-evident that no great interval of time could possibly have elapsed *between* the deposition of these two successive beds, which are so nearly identical in appearance; whereas the common interpretation of evolutionary geology said that a vast interval of time, represented by many millions of years, is here represented by this insignificant line between two strata which look perfectly conformable, with nothing to show for this long interval, either in the way of erosion or deposition.

Soon afterwards I ran across something even more significant. I found some examples of an exactly similar conformity, but in the reverse order, with the alleged " old " rocks on top, this time, and the " young " strata underneath, but with every physical appearance of having been *actually deposited* in this order of sequence.

A great light began to break in upon my soul. I realized that possibly no fossil form is older or younger than any others intrinsically and necessarily. That is, these buried fossil forms possibly may not represent successive " ages " in the long development of organic life; on the contrary they may all have been living contemporaneously, and may each have been buried in its own locality by whatever caused the geological changes. Accordingly, if a catastrophic interpretation of the geological changes were adopted, and if we do not arbitrarily put some of these fossils in one age of the world's history and some in another, but admit that they may have all lived contemporaneously together, what sort of chance would there be left for a theory of organic evolution under such circumstances?

The two decades or more that have followed have been devoted to an almost continuous study of the problems of organic evolution, with results as shown in my published writings. Some of these writings have been devoted to the moral and religious aspects of the doctrine; others deal exclusively with the geological, the latest of the latter class being a Textbook in which the science has been reconstructed in such a way as to place it inductively on bare facts alone, with the theories separately stated. The present volume is an effort to consider all of the more common biological arguments which are relied upon by evolutionists to prove their theory. While not by any means exhaustive, it is probably the most complete and specific of any of the many books written in recent years against the theory.

There are certain classes of people for whom this book is not intended.

It has not been written primarily for the standpatters in natural science. So far as my observation goes, these men do not read very much on the other side of these questions. For them these are closed questions, not subject to further debate. For instance, when Henry Fairfield Osborn rushed into print in criticism of Bateson's Toronto address, deploring that such an address had been given and saying that it tended to " confuse " the public regarding the facts of organic evolution, he naively displayed by statements in this attack itself that he had not at that time read Bateson's address. And, of course, it would be quite too much to hope that such standpat evolutionists would ever condescend to read such a work as this, except *sub rosa*.

These men have long had a quarrel with me regarding the manner in which these new views are being presented. They say that these alleged new scientific facts have not been presented in the regular or ethical way, that is, through the standard scientific journals first of all. And they scornfully refuse to consider alleged facts which have not been first approved by some scientific society, or published in "orthodox" scientific journals, but which have first been issued in popular or even in *religious* periodicals.

But how shall we ever make any progress in a further understanding of these matters, if the regular scientific channels are kept closed to the presentation of new ideas which seem heretical to scientific orthodoxy, and then all "reputable" scientists refuse to read or consider any new facts or new ideas which are presented in any other way?

Twenty-five years ago, when I first made some of my revolutionary discoveries in geology, I was confronted with this very problem of how these new ideas were to be presented to the public. And it was only after I found that the regular channels of publication were denied me, that I decided to use the many other doors which stood wide open. Perhaps I made a mistake. Perhaps I should have had more regard to the etiquette of scientific pedantry, and should have stood humbly hat in hand before the editorial doors which had been banged in my face more than once. But I decided otherwise, with a full realization of the consequences; and I have not yet seen any reason for thinking that I really made a mistake. Some day it may appear that the reigning clique of "reputable" scientists have never had a monopoly of the facts of nature.

Secondly, this book is not intended for that large class of "progressive" theologians who claim that religion is merely a matter of internal, psychological experience, that it does not have anything to do with the objective facts of natural science, nor do the latter have anything to do with religion. People who are obsessed by this bias or prejudice derived from the Kantian philosophy cannot be expected to attend to any such objective evidence as may be here presented. A complementary class is found among scientists, who affect to ignore any line of argument which brings God or the truths of religion into correlation with scientific facts. But I cannot thus put asunder what God has joined together; to me religion and objective facts are only different aspects of one great unity; and I believe that any method of handling any subject is correct and proper, providing it adheres to the well-recognized canons of logical and philosophical method. I regret to say that many of my fellow scientists have so confined themselves to some narrow specialty that they are not at home in any general discussion of the broader aspects of such a topic as this of organic evolution.

Nor is this book intended for those people with chiefly a religious or a literary education who affect to ignore the discoveries of objective science. Such persons would take no interest in the argument presented in the following pages. Not only are they oblivious of the apparently strong arguments which have hitherto been relied upon to establish the doctrine of organic evolution in opposition to the Bible doctrine of creation, but most of them are quite unaware that any conflict between these ideas has been in progress. Such people may as well sleep on, amusing themselves in their dreams with the scholastic pedantries of a bygone age.

But this book is written for all those candid people among scientific workers who still have open minds and are not cocksure regarding the dogmas which have been taught for two generations in the name of natural science, who are not quite certain that the doctrine of organic evolution is forever a closed question upon which no further light need be expected. It is also written for those among the so-called " Fundamentalists " who wish to be informed regarding the strictly scientific aspects of those main questions which are in dispute between them and the " Modernists." A third class of readers may be included, namely, the great general public, who may not belong to either camp, but who have heard the ringing battle-cries of the leading champions of the conflicting hosts, and who wish further information as to what it is all about.

G. McC. P.

UNION COLLEGE, NEBRASKA.

Contents

"Phylogeny, *i. e.*, reconstruction of what has happened in the past, is no science, but a product of fantastic speculations."

J. P. LOTSY,
Evolution by Means of Hybridization.

"If one scans a bit thoughtfully the landscape of human life for the last few decades, he can hardly fail to see signs that the whole battle ground of evolution will have to be fought over again; this time not so much between scientists and theologians, as among scientists themselves."

WILLIAM EMERSON RITTER,
The University of California.

QUO VADIMUS?

I

THE theory of organic evolution has itself gone through an evolution or development. If we speak of its modern form as having begun with Buffon (1707-88), Erasmus Darwin (1731-1802), Lamarck (1744-1829), or Oken (1776-1851), we may well speak of its having reached its culmination about the beginning of the present century, and as being now well along in its decline. It is still taught (or taken for granted) by all college and high school text-books dealing with biological subjects; but in every single department of natural science, those arguments which formerly were relied upon to prove organic development from the moneron to man, have been quietly undermined and discredited by modern discoveries. Soon after the beginning of the dispute between the Neo-Lamarckians and the followers of Weismann regarding the inheritance of acquired characters, Sir William Dawson declared that Darwin's theory seemed to have entered upon a process of disintegration. But with the progress of discovery we have witnessed this disintegration at work with the other parts of the general theory, such as the methods and the limits of variation, and especially the geological concept of a definite historical series of plants and animals in a well-defined order, which is the indispensable outline upon which any scheme of organic development must be built.

The first criticisms of the evolutionary scheme of geology appeared in 1902 and 1906, with works by the present writer. Gradually this attack on the evolutionary outline of geology gathered strength; but it seems doubtful if any mere academic objection to the theory would ever have effected the overthrow of an idea which had become so integral a part of all biological thinking. It was the religious aspects of the revolt against the theory which gave it strength, just as it had been the atheistic implications of Darwinism as an "Anti-Genesis," to use Haeckel's term, which in the first instance had made the theory so popular during the closing decades of the nineteenth century. To-day it is largely the religious implications of the problem which still make it a popular subject of discussion.

But the problem of organic evolution is primarily a scientific problem, and ought to be discussed as such. I am never ashamed to point out the bearings of scientific facts and theories upon religious truths; but in the following chapters the discussion will be carried on along scientific lines, scientific reasons alone being adduced as proof, and the evidence of well-known scientists alone being brought forward in support of the facts presented.

II

But a remarkable situation must be pointed out in this connection.

The recent discussion of the differences between the Modernists and the Fundamentalists has brought out the curious fact that the ones who pride themselves on their modernness are nevertheless aligning themselves with the reactionaries in science. For there are two quite distinct classes among scientists, so far as their attitude toward the problem of organic evolution is concerned. And it is surely an interesting phenomenon to note that the friends of the Bible, who have been accused of having a " static " religion, are nevertheless progressives in their attitude toward modern science; while the so-called " Modernists " are as static or reactionary in their science as they are " progressive " in their religion.

The obscurantist or reactionary group among biological scientists may be illustrated by such men as Henry Fairfield Osborn, J. McKeen Cattell, Edwin Grant Conklin, H. H. Newman, Vernon Kellogg, and Karl Pearson. These with many others may be regarded as the Old Guard, the standpatters, regarding the doctrine of organic evolution. The real progressives among modern scientists may be represented by such men as William Bateson, Thomas Hunt Morgan, Hugo de Vries, J. P. Lotsy, J. C. Willis, H. B. Guppy, Arthur Willey, J. T. Cunningham, and D. H. Scott, men who, though still retaining a general faith in the doctrine of organic development *somehow*, very clearly and very positively tell us that they do not know *how* any such progressive development among animals and plants could possibly have come about.

For many years members of the Old Guard have adopted a very lofty air toward their opponents. They have systematically ignored all opposing arguments which have been directed against the theory as a whole, though freely discussing any objections offered by " reputable " scientists against any of the various details. But this lofty method of ignoring all direct opposition becomes suspicious when the opposing arguments have attained their present proportions. For it now becomes a question whether the reason for ignoring these arguments is not really a fear to meet them in the open. Furthermore, the ignorance which the Old Guard have been fond of charging against their opponents may have another side to it. In the present state of modern science, ignorance of biology and geology means chiefly an ignorance of the wealth of solid scientific arguments against the theory of organic evolution. Evolutionists may not be so anxious for Fundamentalists to become familiar with the facts of biology and geology, when they realize that these modern facts are being used against them and their theories.

For the evolutionists to keep on ignoring these modern scientific objections to the theory of evolution, may be an indication of their shrewdness; but for the friends of the Bible to keep on ignoring them would be an indication of stupidity. For it is a fact that the modern discoveries in heredity and variation, in embryology, and in geology, make the case against organic evolution vastly stronger than even most Fundamentalists have supposed; and it is to a study of these various subdivisions of the subject that the reader is invited in the following chapters.

III

In other words, all the important lines of argument which have commonly been put forward as evidence in favor of organic evolution will need to be considered in the following pages. They will include such lines of study as:—

1. *Genetics.* — Under this subject will be given the pertinent facts which are now known regarding such subjects as *variation, adaptation,* etc. The modern discoveries along these lines are the causes which have brought both Darwinism and Lamarckism into such disrepute as true explanations of *how* evolution has come about. But they leave untouched the larger or more general problem of evolution *somehow*.

2. *Paleontology.* — The evidence supposed to be furnished by the fossils has for over a hundred years been the real *raison d' être* for any and all theories of organic evolution. The writings of the present author were the first in modern times to point out the false logic of the current geological theories, as well as many examples and facts which are wholly inconsistent with the evolutionary arrangement of the fossils, upon which as an outline the theory of organic evolution has always been built. Only a mere outline of the geological argument can be presented in the present work; the details of this argument will be found elsewhere in the published works of the present writer.

3. *Embryology.* — The remarkable facts brought to light by the study of the developing embryo during the early part of the nineteenth century, were scarcely second in importance as giving an impetus to the general idea of organic development. Under the enthusiastic tutelage of Louis Agassiz, the world was asked to look at the wonderful parallelism between the growth of the individual from the one-celled stage (ontogeny), the alleged succession in time of the related species (phylogeny), and the present classification of the modern forms in a systematic arrangement (taxonomy); and there is little wonder that in the hands of Haeckel and others this " argument from comparison " became one of the very strongest, the one utterly unanswerable argument, which always left the opponent or objector dumb with a nameless stupefaction.

As we look back upon this argument and this situation from the vantage ground of two generations of thought and study, we see that the effects of this argument were quite grotesque. How well it illustrates the fallacy in logic of attempting to prove a *question of fact* by mere *analogy*. Many analogies, as we know, are wholly fallacious; while no analogy can really prove anything at all, it can only illustrate what is already known from other reasons. Thus we see that the overwhelming popularity of this argument was merely an exhibition of the gullibility of the average person, who has usually had little training in logical processes, or who may even have a congenital incapacity for careful, persistent thinking.

With the collapse of the evolutionary arrangement of the fossils, however, the situation has become even more amusing to those who can assume a detached attitude upon the solid facts of science and watch the procession of dupes go by. For it now appears that the geological arrangement of the fossils is in reality only *an artificial scheme,* after all, just merely an ancient taxonomic series of the total forms of life formerly living on the globe. Thus we have *two* artificial series, in the above mentioned argument of Haeckel, and only *one* real or objective series. In this view of the case, it becomes a real intellectual amusement to watch the methods employed by Haeckel, Romanes, Le Conte, and others, in proving their theory of organic development. And accordingly, this argument from embryology has lost all its force for every one who has arrived at the sophisticated view of geology and paleontology.

4. *Natural Selection.*— A separate chapter is here given to the theory of natural selection. Not that this theory ever contributed any logical support to the general doctrine of organic evolution; and not that in this middle of the third decade of the twentieth century any formal refutation of this theory is needed. A dead lion needs no bullet. Nevertheless, this doctrine has so permeated modern thinking in history, in sociology, in pedagogy, to say nothing of theology, and in so many ways is this theory bound up with the general concept of organic evolution, that a separate and formal treatment seems advisable.

IV

Fifty years ago, or even twenty-five years ago, many thousands of well-meaning Christians would have been glad to make peace with the theory of evolution by a compromise. Many were willing to concede evolution as the origin of the plants and animals, if only a real creation were left for man himself. We now realize that this compromise was quite uncalled for. To-day there can be no thought of compromise in this way on the part of any one who is even moderately informed regarding the present scientific situation. All the groups of well-ascertained facts (in distinction from pure speculations) are now seen to be on the side of the doctrine of a literal Creation of all the great groups or kinds of plants and animals, and against any scheme of explaining the origin of these larger groups which could properly be called a process of organic evolution.

As a whole, the theory of organic development

from the protozoa to man is a blunder, an utterly impossible scheme, if the new evidence of geology be given any consideration.   True, atheistic materialism will always continue to deny the possibility of a world cataclysm; but even with this denial, in the light of the exposure of the false logic and pseudo-scientific methods in the evolutionary arrangement of the fossils, organic evolution can no longer hold up its head among the reputable sciences founded on facts and logic.

Organic evolution is dead, so far as thousands of intelligent people are concerned.   This volume is merely a sort of funeral oration.   *Requiescat in pace.*

BIBLIOGRAPHY

(Pro-Evolutionary)

Kellogg, V. L., *Darwinism To-day;* 1893.
                 Evolution the Way of Man; 1924.
Le Conte, Joseph, *Evolution and Religious Thought;* 1899.
Newman, H. H., *Readings in Evolution, Genetics, and Eugenics;* 1922.
Romanes, G. J., *Darwin and After Darwin;* 1892.
Scott, W. B., *The Theory of Evolution;* 1917.
Thomson, J. Arthur (Editor), *The Outline of Science,* 4 vols.; 1922.
Van Loon, H., *The Story of Mankind;* 1921.
Wells, H. G., *The Outline of History,* 2 vols.; 1920.

II

THE NEXT GENERATION

I

IF we cross a tall pea (*Pisum sativum*) with a dwarf, both pure bred, we always get all talls in the first hybrid generation. There are no dwarfs, and no intermediates. And it makes no difference whether the pollen came from the tall and the ovule from the dwarf, or *vice versa*. In the language of the new science of genetics, the tall factor or character is said to be *dominant,* and the dwarf character is *recessive.* But when we plant the seed from these new hybrid talls, the plants of the second hybrid generation always show a tendency to split up into talls and dwarfs. We always get 25 per cent which are talls and prove to be pure bred, breeding true ever afterwards; 25 per cent which are dwarfs and breed true; and 50 per cent which are talls, but by further propagation show themselves to be hybrids, breaking up in the next generation in just the same proportion as was stated for the first hybrid generation. And like Tennyson's " Brook," this process will go on forever, and can be tested out by any person in any part of the world.

Similarly, if we cross a black and a white (albino) guinea pig, we always get all blacks in the first hybrid generation; and it makes no difference whether it was the father or the mother that was black. But in the next generation we get 25 per cent pure bred blacks; 25 per cent pure bred whites, just as pure bred in respect to their future progeny as if they had come from a thousand generations of unmixed ancestry; and 50 per cent which will be black in colour, but which will prove to be hybrids, breaking up in the next generation in the very same mathematical proportions as before.

On the other hand, if we cross a black and a white Andalusian fowl, we get something which seems at first glance to be different from the results just stated. For in the first hybrid generation the chicks are a queer mixture of colour, called "blue" by poultry men. In this case it seems that neither factor has been dominant, but that each has been of about the same potency. However, in the next generation we get the same old percentage, 25 per cent pure bred black, 25 per cent pure bred white, and 50 per cent hybrid blue. And thus it goes on ever afterward. In reality this case is not at all different from the one mentioned above; the apparent difference has come about because neither the blackness nor the whiteness was dominant, each proved to be equal to the other.

II

These facts illustrate the great principle that the various characters or factors of plants and animals are transmitted separately and unblemished in heredity. And the great wonder is that we did not find this out hundreds of years ago.

Thousands of colours, shapes, sizes, and whatnots in plants and animals have now been quite fully investigated according to these laws; with the result that we are now beginning to know something quite definite about combinations of factors or characters in plants and animals, just as we have already learned about a great many combinations which we can make in chemistry. Of course, our knowledge of the possible combinations in plants and animals does not at all approach the completeness which our knowledge has reached in chemistry. Doubtless it never will be as complete; for these combinations among living creatures are a much more complicated process, and the difficulties in the way of biological experiments to illustrate all these combinations are a million times greater than in chemistry. But the two classes of combinations, the biological and the chemical, seem to resemble each other very closely, and the one class of phenomena is evidently just as much a matter of law as is the other.

All these results among plants and animals have been worked out long since the day of Charles Darwin. They are known as Mendelism; and were first brought to the attention of the world at large about twenty-four years ago. Since that time these new principles have completely changed the views and the theories of the scientific world regarding heredity. One of the assumptions made by Charles Darwin in building up his theory of organic evolution, was that plants and animals naturally tend to vary in all directions and to an unlimited degree. He recognized no law in connection with variation, for in his day no such law was known. But Mendelism is now showing us quite definitely *how* plants and animals vary. Just as definitely the new science of heredity is showing us the precise limits of these variations, and the limits of the possibilities in the way of the hereditary transmission of characters. And as Edwin Grant

Conklin has said, " At present it is practically certain that there is no other kind of inheritance than Mendelian."

III

The Darwinists used to emphasize the fact that no two individuals are exactly alike, that not even two leaves on the same tree are alike. All this is true; but we now see that this general fact has a very different meaning from that which Darwin read from it. We now know that these variations or differences between individuals of the same species are of two kinds, quite distinct from each other:

1. Individual variations, or *fluctuations*, as the scientists term them, which seem to be caused by the environment, that is by differences in heat or cold, in the amount of food, or by some other unknown factor. But these fluctuations never prove to be hereditary; that is, they are never passed along to the next generation.

2. The other kind of variations are termed *mutations* or *modifications,* which are born with the individual plant or animal, which are the result of inheritance, and which are faithfully passed along in heredity either as dominant or as recessive characters.

The changes which are induced in the plant or the animal during its lifetime, spoken of as the effects of its environment, that is, produced by variations in temperature, by good food or bad, by exercise or the lack of it,—all such changes are mere *fluctuations*, and are *not* passed along in heredity to the next generation. To use the current scientific phraseology, all such variations are " acquired characters;" and scientists are quite agreed that acquired characters are never transmitted in heredity. This is the same principle as the well-known impossibility of perpetual motion. A wheel by its turning is never seen to work up more and more speed, or more and more energy of rotation, merely by its turning, and by itself. It takes some external force even to keep it going. And it seems to be one of the best established principles of biology that the effects of the environment are never passed along from one generation to the next, unless in a few ambiguous cases which are clearly cases of degeneracy.

On the other hand, all distinct characters or factors, whether of form, or size, or colour, or whatever, are *modifications;* and they are always faithfully carried along in heredity, according to the principles above mentioned which are now universally known as Mendel's laws.

IV

When these new ideas regarding heredity were presented about a quarter of a century ago, they met with a great deal of incredulity and opposition on the part of scientists; for they were very clearly contrary to what was at that time considered to be absolute scientific fact. The ideas then current, received from Darwin and his immediate successors, had made no provision for such facts as these; and it took a considerable time for biologists to get their bearings with reference to these new facts. However, the students of heredity have long since made up a *modus vivendi* in view of these new principles; and to-day these discoveries of Gregor Mendel, with some related discoveries which have since been made, completely dominate the whole of biological research in the field of heredity. But the reader must not get the impression that under such a system as that spoken of above there is no room for anything really new. It is true, that when we are dealing with only one pair of contrasted characters at a time, as in all the examples mentioned above, there is not much room for any strictly new types, except in cases similar to that of the blue Andalusian fowls, which are a blending of the two contrasted characters. However, when we come to combine *two pairs* of contrasted characters, there is then room for two wholly new types to appear; and when more than two pairs of contrasted factors are blended there is room for many new types, the number of new types in each instance being capable of exact arithmetical prediction. For example, if we cross a round yellow pea with a wrinkled green pea, we get all round yellows in the first hybrid generation. This hybrid round yellow pea looks exactly like one of its parents; but this is because roundness of form and yellowness of colour are both dominant characters. That this new pea is really a hybrid is proved in the next generation; for out of every sixteen in this new generation, we get nine round yellows, like the one grandparent, one wrinkled green, like the other grandparent, but three *yellow wrinkled*, and three *round green*,—these latter ones being wholly new kinds, so far as their direct ancestors are concerned. And a certain percentage of these new kinds will always come true to seed, thus proving that they are not hybrids, but pure bred.

But it is evident that these three yellow wrinkled and the three round green peas have been made directly by our method of combination, just as we can make new substances in the chemical laboratory by proper combinations. And if we were to go on to combine *three* pairs of contrasted characters, or more, the result, while still more complicated, can nevertheless be worked out and explained and even predicted with precision, though several quite new types may have been originated in this way. Thomas Hunt Morgan, of Columbia University, one of the leading workers along this line, has produced over two hundred new kinds of the fruit fly (*Drosophila*), almost every organ of the animal having varied in one or more particulars. Plant breeders have also originated many wonderful new types by directed and purposed crossings.

In the year 1910, a red sunflower was discovered growing by the side of the road near Boulder, Colorado. Now the sunflower is peculiar in that it must have pollen from some other individual plant in order for its seeds to be fertilized, in other words, it must be cross-pollinated in order to develop perfect seeds. But there were no other red sunflowers with which to cross this stranger. So it was crossed with an ordinary yellow. Fortunately, the red colour proved to be dominant; and several pure bred reds were obtained.

Sometime before this, the English growers had developed a so-called " primrose " sunflower—a very light or straw-coloured yellow. What would happen if this primrose sunflower should be crossed with one of these pure bred reds? The crossing was done; but, sad to say, nothing but reds developed. This was clearly disappointing; and if the experimenters had not known anything about Mendelism, or if all this had happened under the old regime of " pure Darwinism " of fifty years ago, probably the experiment would not have been carried any further.

But the experiment was continued; these disappointing reds were allowed to cross, and their seeds were planted. And in the next generation two wholly new types appeared or were separated out, as the Men-delians say. A certain percentage of the total plants proved to be red, like one pair; another percentage was primrose-coloured, like the other pair. But there were two kinds which showed a surprising colouration; a certain percentage was of a wine-red or old-rose colour; while another certain percentage was of a dark orange colour. Of course, both the old-rose and orange sunflowers were wholly new types. It is probably safe to say that such colours in sunflowers had never been seen on earth before; for such combinations as produced them can hardly be imagined to occur in the wild state. Yet if either of these types had been found growing wild and we had not known its method of origin, and especially if this new and strange colour had been accompanied (as it might easily have been) by new forms of leaf or of other habits of growth, we should without doubt have called it a *new species;* and scientists are now agreed that probably hundreds and thousands of just such Mendelian segregates have been listed and described as new species, among plants, and birds, and insects.

In addition to the principles brought out above, we occasionally see what are termed " sports," or " mutations " arising suddenly in some way that cannot well be accounted for. J. P. Lotsy is of the opinion that the only source of variation of any kind is through hybridization, or through the crossing of contrasted unit characters. Other biologists do not agree with him; but it is not known how or why these sports or natural mutations do arise, if not because of some combination of the factors of heredity. At any rate, when such sports or mutations do arise, they obey the law of

Mendelian inheritance in all subsequent tests of breeding.

By means of combinations suggested by these new principles of heredity, many hundreds of new kinds of plants and animals have been manufactured in the seed patch or in the breeding pen; and these modern methods of breeding have introduced rule and system into the old hit-and-miss methods of former days. Doubtless we have thus produced very many kinds which if found wild in nature would forthwith have been listed as " new species." The work of Hall and Clements, as recently published in their monograph, *The Phylogenetic Method in Taxonomy,* has shown that our classification lists are overburdened with great numbers of distinct " species " which are nothing but Mendelian segregates, which will not stand the tests of breeding. As Professor William Bateson said in his address before the British Association at Toronto, December 28, 1921: " Plenty of Mendelian combinations would in nature pass the scrutiny of even an exacting systematist, and be given ' specific rank.' "

V

But where are we, in the light of these new facts? Have we at last solved the old problem of the origin of species? Do these principles let us into the secret of how new types of life have really originated in nature in the long ago? And is it true that now we need only to project these modern laws and processes back far enough into the past to account for not only species, but genera, and orders, and classes? In short, does this new view of nature help us to see how any one distinct type of life may have originated from some quite different type of life?

When the laws of Mendelian combinations were first made familiar to the world at the beginning of the present century, many loudly proclaimed that the riddle had at last been solved.   But further experiments and further study of the real results thus obtained have dashed the hopes of those who were looking to these new facts of genetics for light on the general problem of organic evolution.

As a recent biological writer has stated the matter:

" I well remember the enthusiasm with which the Mendelian theory was received, when it was introduced to the scientific world in the early years of this century.   We thought that at last the key to evolution had been discovered. As a leading Mendelian put it, whilst the rest of us had been held up by an apparently impenetrable hedge, namely, the difficulty of explaining the origin of variation, Mendel had, unnoticed, cut a way through.   But, as our knowledge of the facts grew, the difficulty of using Mendelian phenomena to explain evolution, became apparent, and this early hope sickened and died.   The way which Mendel cut was seen to lead into a *cul-de-sac*." (E. W. MacBride, *Science Progress,* January, 1922.)

Evidently the plain facts brought to light by experimental breeding are not much to the liking of the people who call themselves the representatives of the old traditions.   Mendelism seems to be getting them nowhere, except up a blind alley, into a *cul-de-sac*.

Robert Heath Lock gives us a very candid summary of the results of Mendelian breeding:

" On the mind of a biologist familiar with what was known of heredity only about twenty years ago, these facts must fall with a sense of complete novelty.   The ideas current even so short a time ago are not so much extended, or even altered, as replaced by an entirely new set of ideas. And it may be remarked in passing that the biologist of fifty years ago and more was much nearer to our present line of inquiry." (*Variation, Heredity, and Evolution,* pp. 225-226; 1920.)

Lock was a botanist; and it is well known that as a class the botanists have been much less free in accepting the doctrine of organic evolution. In his presidential address before the Botanical Section of the British Association, at the Liverpool Meeting in 1923, A. G. Tansley stated that in the light of recent developments in botany the search for common ancestors among the great groups of plants would seem to be " literally a hopeless quest, the genealogical tree an illusory vision " (*Nature,* March 8, 1924; p. 356).

In commenting on these pronouncements of Tansley, Prof. F. O. Bower, of the University of Glasgow, declared:

" At the present moment we seem to have reached a phase of negation in respect of the achievements of phyletic morphology, and in conclusions as to descent." And he adds: " I believe that a similar negative attitude is also to be found among those who pursue zoological science." (*Ib. id.*)

In view of such statements as these, one is surprised at the confident assertions of the public broadcasters of the evolution dogma, that all scientists are agreed regarding the stability of the theory of organic evolution. Perhaps so; but it rather appears to me that these confident assertions of the evolutionary advocates are more like the whistling of small boys in the dark, a psychological device to keep up their own courage.

VI

Prof. Paul Kammerer, of the University of Vienna, as might be expected, also takes the ground that the discoveries connected with Mendelism offer us no help in solving the problem of how species have originated. In a recent publication he thus expresses the present situation:

> " Aside from very limited fluctuations around a fixed center, the predispositions of these characteristics cannot become greater or less and cannot be changed at all. Just as innumerable masterpieces of music are assembled from a few fundamental tones, just as a few fundamental tints magically reproduce multicoloured reality, so is the ability of the living world to assume different forms derived from comparatively few fundamentals."

He goes on to say that the present tendency in biology is to emphasize the unchangeableness of types; that what little change is admitted " would be much too limited to bring about a development of species, and even still more limited to create even larger groups and classes.

> " The theory of evolution at the present time is pointing in that direction; it is returning to the theory of non-evolution." (*Literary Review*, Feb. 23, 1924; p. 538.)

Of course, Kammerer thinks that this tendency toward non-evolution is all wrong; and he argues that only by a return to Lamarckian factors can the doctrine of evolution be again started on the right road. Nevertheless, this testimony is of value in showing the direction of modern tendencies in genetics. Kammerer's own hobby, the alleged transmission in heredity of characters acquired by the parents, is much like the celebrated glamour of light referred to by Wordsworth, it is a phenomenon which never was on sea or land.

VII

Some years before he died, Alfred Russel Wallace stated with some detail the reasons why Mendelism does not help the general theory of organic evolution:

" On the general relation of Mendelism to evolution, I have come to a very definite conclusion. That is, that it has no relation whatever to the evolution of species or higher groups, but is really antagonistic to such evolution. The essential basis of evolution, involving as it does the most minute and all-pervading adaptation to the whole environment, is extreme and ever-present plasticity, as a condition of survival and adaptation. But the essence of Mendelian characters is their rigidity. They are transmitted without variation, and therefore, except by the rarest of accidents, they can never become adapted to ever-varying conditions." (*Letters and Reminiscences,* p. 340.)

VIII

There are really two difficulties in this connection. (1) Natural species, or well defined species as we find them in nature, are quite generally cross-sterile with one another, even when we take considerable pains to make them cross; whereas the new kinds which we have developed under Mendelian methods, or which we have produced under domestication among plants and animals, are almost invariably cross-fertile with one another. Darwin rather made light of this barrier of cross-sterility which nature has erected between natural species; but modern scientists see in this barrier something which we cannot produce artificially in any way, and which we have never yet seen arise under natural methods. In this barrier we seem to have something which quite effectually differentiates natural species from those Mendelian segregates which we can easily produce artificially.

And yet it seems almost certain that very many so-called " species " of the systematists or taxonomists have arisen naturally, even though we may not have hit upon the precise method. As Bateson remarks:

" We may even be certain that numbers of excellent species recognized by entomologists and ornithologists, for example, would, if subjected to breeding tests, be immediately proved to be analytical varieties, differing from each other merely in the presence or absence of definite factors." (Mendel's *Principles of Heredity*, p. 284; 1909.)

Still we do not know how this barrier of cross-sterility which separates most true species as found in nature could have arisen. As Bateson himself expressed it in his Toronto address:

" The production of an indubitably sterile hybrid from completely fertile parents which have arisen under critical observation from a single common origin, is the event for which we wait." (*Science,* January 20, 1922.)

(2) The other difficulty with which we are confronted by Mendelism is even more serious, when we attempt to use these facts regarding heredity to explain the origin of genera, families, orders, classes, and phyla. For we soon find that there are very definite *limits* to the kinds which we can produce in this fashion. We find that we are merely working around within a limited circle; for by back-crossing we can always work back to the original forms with which we started, just as the chemist can always work backwards and get the original compounds with which he began his experiments. And just as the chemist finds that he can never get out of his retorts and test tubes any new element which was not already contained in the compounds with which he has been working, so

does the Mendelian find that, no matter how wide a variety of types he may succeed in producing, he is still within the charmed circle of the original type of life, beyond which it seems impossible to carry any organic changes by either natural or artificial methods.

IX

The meaning of the chromosomes and some of the wonderful facts connected with the developing embryo, will be considered in a subsequent chapter. But it may be worth our while to consider the meaning of the facts which we have been studying.

The believer in the direct creation of the original stocks among plants and animals, from which the present wide diversity has arisen by much splitting or differentiation, may almost be pardoned for an " I told you so," in view of the facts of heredity as we now know them.

Darwin's idea was that all living forms tend to vary in a haphazard fashion and in about all possible directions. He thought also that these small variations would become accumulated in one or more directions which might ultimately prove " useful " to the organism in a new way. And when these accumulated variations had progressed far enough to make the new form essentially different from its original, we would have a " new species." In reality this view of the case now appears to be little else than a burlesque on the real facts of nature. We now know quite definitely *how* plants and animals vary; but these variations are by no means haphazard.

We have already shown that these variations are of two classes, fluctuations, which are never hereditary, and modifications, which always have hereditary possibilities, either as dominants or as recessives. The former are probably the chief ones with which we need to be concerned in any comprehensive scheme of evolution; but they seem to be few in number, and besides there seems to be no method by which several dominant factors can become accumulated together in any one form, so as to make a new type of animal (or plant) which is essentially different from any of its ancestors.

One fact of prime importance in this connection, is that any natural organism, whether plant or animal, seems to possess more potential characters than it can give expression to in any single variety or kind. Thus it becomes necessary for some of these characters to become latent, in order to allow others to be manifested. This tends to permit many variations within the bounds of the species. But this specific elasticity as thus exhibited seems to be very definitely limited within comparatively narrow lines beyond which we have never yet seen a single type pass under either natural or artificial conditions. We can produce variations galore; but when we have made them we can repeat the process over and over again with the very same results; and we can by back-crossing return to the original forms with which we started, just as we can in the case of a chemical compound. Hence the believer in creation may well ask, where is the evolution in all this? Or how do these facts of heredity throw any light on the problem of the origin of real kinds, any more than our manipulation of chemical compounds throws light on the origin of the elements? Quite obviously, in biology as in chemistry, we are only working within a definitely limited circle, merely marking time.

And we can now better understand another remark by Professor William Bateson, to the effect that, " had Mendel's work come into the hands of Darwin, it is not too much to say that the history of the development of evolutionary philosophy would have been very different from that which we have witnessed."

X

The present situation in biology was well stated by Dr. D. H. Scott, the paleobotanist, in his address before the British Association in 1921, where he said:

"At present all speculation on the nature of past changes is in the air, for variation itself is only an hypothesis, and we have to decide, quite arbitrarily, what kind of variations we think may probably have occurred in the course of descent." (*Nature,* Sept. 29, 1921.)

He went on to say that, " For the moment, at all events, the Darwinian period is past; we can no longer enjoy the comfortable assurance, which once satisfied so many of us, that the main problem had been solved —all is again in the melting-pot." He thought, however, that the general idea of evolution still remains, " even if we hold it only as an act of faith," because he said that the evidence of paleontology is still unshaken. Whether this is true or not we shall see in the next chapter.

XI

However, it may be well to note in passing that not all of our leading scientists have retained their confidence in evolutionary pedigrees based on the fossils. Dr. J. P. Lotsy, the Holland botanist, expresses himself as follows:

"Phylogeny, *i. e.* reconstruction of what has happened in the past, is no science, but a product of fantastic speculations." (*Evolution by Means of Hybridization,* p. 140; 1916.)

And he seeks to emphasize this point in the following language:

"Those who know that I have spent a considerable part of my life in efforts to trace the phylogeny of the vegetable kingdom, will know that this is not written down lightly; nobody cares to destroy his own efforts." (*Ib., id.*)

It is worthy of note that Dr. D. H. Scott, in his most recent book, while protesting that Lotsy has probably gone a little too far, adds:

"Like Dr. Lotsy, I have become skeptical of late as to most phylogenetic reconstructions." (*Extinct Plants,* etc., p. 18; 1924.)

Furthermore, Prof. A. C. Seward, of Cambridge University, tells us that "The present tendency is to discard the old-fashioned genealogical tree with its wonderful diversity of branches," as at all a suitable method of picturing the course of organic development. For he says that "a student who takes an impartial retrospect soon discovers that the fossil record raises more problems than it solves." (*Nature,* April 26, 1924.)

These are clear and unambiguous statements; and they are from the very leading botanists of the world. And it should be remembered that these statements are made by these men quite apart from the damaging evidence which has been presented by the present writer in his various works, a summary of which will be presented in the next chapter.

XII

Another summary of the present situation was given by Bateson before the American Association, at Toronto, December 28, 1921. Parts of this address have been often quoted from, but the points which are of interest to us in this connection are well summarized in the following:

> "We cannot see how the differentiation into species came about. Variation of many kinds, often considerable, we daily witness, but no origin of species . . . Meanwhile, though our faith in evolution stands unshaken, we have no acceptable account of the origin of 'species.'" (*Science,* Jan. 20, 1922.)

XIII

The definite conclusions which we may draw from all this welter of discussion and experimentation are not ambiguous, nor are they of small importance to the general problem of organic evolution. We seem to have in nature certain great groups of living creatures, call them what we will, genera, families, or tribes, but usually *larger than the "species,"* all the members of each of which have probably descended from common ancestors. Within any of these great groups new types have appeared repeatedly, and may appear again under suitable conditions. Such new types, however, never seem to get outside the limits of the original types, strictly speaking. Possibly, under the very peculiar conditions subsisting immediately after the great world-cataclysm revealed to us by geology, distinct kinds ("species") may have split off or may have become differentiated in ways or to an extent which we have never yet succeeded in duplicating by any of our experiments in genetics; but even these seem properly to be well within the bounds of those original stocks from which these species or genera arose. As we shall see later, the *Family* seems to be generally the original unit. But as for attempting to explain by the known

laws of heredity and variation the origin of the families, orders, classes, and phyla, this notion seems utterly fantastic and unscientific.

In other words, each of these great groups of plants
or animals (genera or families), seems to be a strictly
closed system, allowing of considerable variations
within the system, but definitely limited in the number
and the extent of these possible variations.

Thomas Hunt Morgan has told us how these principles work out in the case of the Mendelian segregates of *Drosophila*, when he shows that the same
mutant type has appeared over and over again. He
says:

"It has long been known, in a general way, that the same
kinds of mutants reappear *in the same species*. We are now
beginning to get evidence from pedigree cultures that the
same types may occur *in different species* . . . [They are
called] identical mutants . . . Such a case has arisen between
the two species of *Drosophila simulans* and *melanogaster*.
Sturtevant has shown that there are thirteen mutants that
are the same in both species . . .

"If, then, it can be established beyond dispute that similarity or even identity of the same character in different
species is not always to be interpreted to mean that both have
arisen from a common ancestor, the whole argument from
comparative anatomy built upon the descent theory seems to
tumble in ruins." (*Scientific Monthly,* March, 1923; p. 246.)

It is true, Dr. Morgan proceeds immediately to dis-
claim the latter suggestion, remarking that the inevitable ruin of the whole argument based on comparative
anatomy is only "a first impression." On the contrary, this impression seems to stay by me for a long
time; though I am willing to admit that with this evidence we must suppose the two species here spoken
of, *simulans* and *melanogaster*, have had a common

origin, and are themselves only equivalent to Mendelian segregates.

But I cannot shake off the conviction that in all these Mendelian experiments we are only working within very definite limits, tramping over the same old ground time after time, though occasionally finding some little nook or corner which has not been hitherto explored.

XIV

No wonder the doctrinaire evolutionists are growing very impatient with these evident implications of the Mendelian results. In addition to the opinion of E. W. MacBride, already quoted, that these new methods of investigating heredity have led biologists into a *cul-de-sac*, the same author also declares that Morgan's mutations " are pathological in character and have no analogy with the differences between natural races and species." Even Prof. W. Johannsen, of Denmark, seems to be of about the same opinion, and says that " The problem of species-evolution does not seem to be approached seriously through Mendelism nor through the related modern experiences in mutations " (*Nature*, January 12, 1924; pp. 50, 51).

However, to the real seeker after the ultimate truth of nature, these discoveries and tendencies are very illuminating. It is only the ardent believers in organic evolution to whom this whole subject seems distasteful, who complain that Mendelism has led them into a *cul-de-sac*, and that the problem of species-evolution does not seem to be approached seriously by these great fundamental facts regarding the heredity of all living things.

Far from being of assistance in support of the theory of organic evolution, the laws of Mendelian breeding are now seen to be among the strongest proofs against those theories about the origin of plants and animals which have so long been taught to the world under the name of Charles Darwin.

Julian S. Huxley has recently expressed his impatience at the indifference or even the active hostility toward Mendelian investigations displayed by many students of evolutionary problems.   In a recent number of *Nature* he has expressed himself as follows:

"It is a matter of constant surprise why many who profess themselves Darwinian of the Darwinians should not only not avail themselves of the new tool [Mendelism], but also evince positive hostility to it. The new principles are, indeed, the only tool we at present possess which is capable of putting evolutionary theories to experimental test. Yet, with a few honourable exceptions, most taxonomists and 'evolutionists' prefer to stick to speculative methods—speculative because incapable of being tested either by experiment or by calculation—and make no attempt to use the new principles in experimental work,—or, for that matter, even in interpretation."   (*Nature,* April 12, 1924; p. 520.)

No doubt the opponents of Mendelism are right. These modern methods in experimental breeding are a nuisance; for they do not get us anywhere in explaining organic evolution. These standpat evolutionists had better stick to their " speculative methods." By discarding the results obtained from the seed patch and the breeding pen they can go on in their dreaming, without ever awaking to the uncomfortable feeling that they have been running up a blind alley, a scientific *cul-de-sac.*

BIBLIOGRAPHY

Bateson, Wm., *Mendel's Principles of Heredity;* 1909.

Bishop, T. B., *Evolution Criticised;* 1918.

Bower, F. O., *The Present Outlook on Descent; Nature,* March 8, 1924.

Conklin, E. G., *Heredity and Environment;* 1921.

De Vries, Hugo, *Die Mutationstheorie;* 1901.

Lock, Robert Heath, *Variation, Heredity, and Environment;* 1920.

Lotsy, J. P., *Evolution by Means of Hybridization;* 1916.

Morgan, Thos. Hunt, and others, *The Mechanism of Mendelian Heredity,* Revised Edition; 1922.

Morgan, T. H., *The Bearing of Mendelism on the Origin of Species; Scientific Monthly,* March, 1923.

Newman, H. H., *Readings in Evolution, Genetics, and Eugenics;* 1922.

Punnett, R. C., *Mendelism;* 1911.

III

THE STONES THAT CRY OUT

I

THE most serious mistake made by Charles Darwin was his misplaced confidence in Lyellism. It will be remembered that Darwin as a young man had eagerly read Lyell's *Principles of Geology*, that he had taken a copy of this work with him on his voyage in the *Beagle*, and that to the memory of Lyell he had dedicated his record of the discoveries which he made during this trip. And there is no doubt that the geological picture of a long series of successive forms of life in ever-ascending and increasing complexity and perfection of organization, was the ever-present idea in Darwin's mind on which he undertook to build his scheme of organic evolution. It should also be remembered that Huxley declared Lyell's system of uniformitarian geology to be "the chief agent in smoothing the road for Darwin," so far as he himself was concerned, and so far as multitudes of others were concerned who reasoned just as he did.

In our day, when the biological argument has been quite thoroughly investigated and has proved very disappointing, it is this background of the successive forms of developing life which constitutes "by all odds the strongest evidence that we have in favour of organic evolution," as Thomas Hunt Morgan has declared. But in the light of the facts as we now know them, this confidence of Charles Darwin in the accuracy of this long, developing line of geological life-forms, is now seen to have been a mistake,—a case of misplaced confidence. And I have said that this was the most serious mistake made by Darwin, in spite of his complete ignorance of the laws of heredity, as Mendelism has now revealed them to us.

It is now almost a century since Charles Lyell first formulated and developed his system of uniformitarian geology. As we look back upon it from this vantage ground of the accumulated discoveries of nearly a hundred years, the actual amount of knowledge which was then possessed by scientists regarding those facts upon which geology must be built, is seen to have been most pitifully small and meagre. At that time Lyell and his fellows knew nothing of the conditions prevailing at the bottom of the ocean. Our knowledge of the conditions prevailing over three-fourths of our world may be said to have begun with the explorations of the *Challenger* Expedition, in 1872. Not only was Lyell ignorant of the conditions prevailing over the ocean bottom, he was also obsessed with the dogmatic prejudice inherited from Cuvier that essentially all of the plants and animals found as fossils in the rocks were " extinct species," quite different from the somewhat similar forms living in our modern world. This prejudice about " extinct " species was in its turn based on an extremely narrow and unsound theory, likewise inherited from Cuvier, about the " fixity " or unchangeableness of species. It is true, that even now we are still quite unacquainted with the forms of life prevailing over large parts of Africa, or South America or Asia; but we have at least discovered many thousands of brachiopods, or mollusks, or crustaceans, or whatnot in various parts of the world which are *identical* with corresponding fossil forms buried in the rocks of North America, or England, or Japan, or Australia.

In another respect also we now see that Lyell was mistaken. He was quite convinced that there are now slow processes of diastrophism prevailing all over the globe. By diastrophism is meant the theory that the coasts are in places moving upward or downward with reference to the ocean at a slow, gradual rate; and Lyell's doctrine of uniformity was largely based on the evidences which he accumulated to prove this doctrine. Upon this doctrine Lyell built up his system of uniformity; and his thought was that if these hypothetical changes of level around the coasts could be prolonged over a sufficient length of time, the bottom of the ocean might become dry land, or the land might in turn become the bottom of the ocean; and this would then explain why we now find sea creatures as entombed fossils in the limestones and shales of our plains and mountains.

I do not have the space here to enter upon this subject fully. The reader will find the matter considered at length in Chapter XIII of my textbook, *The New Geology*. To this work also the reader is referred for a statement of the facts now known which disprove the theory that the various kinds of fossil animals and plants have existed in a definite chronological or historical order over the earth in the long ago. This latter was, as I have said, the thing upon which Charles Darwin built up his scheme of organic evolution, and as I have remarked above this constituted his most serious mistake.

II

It would be an interesting study to trace the development in Darwin's mind of this idea of organic evolution, for he no doubt owed much to the speculations of his grandfather, Erasmus Darwin, quite as much as he owed to the theories of his predecessors, such as Robert Chambers, Lamarck, Cuvier, Buffon, and many others. We have not the space to enter upon these enticing investigations. We are here concerned chiefly with a brief account of the general lessons to be learned from a study of the whole field of fossil forms as revealed to us by modern geology.

The great comprehensive fact in this connection is that over great areas of our globe we find rocks now composing plains or mountain elevations which were once laid down by moving water, in most cases obviously ocean water, since these rocks contain fossils or forms of life which live in the ocean and some of which live only in the deeper parts of the ocean. The great problem of geology is to tell *how* these world-changes have been brought about. Lyellism says that the changes of ocean and land were regular and gradual or slow, similar to changes which are said to be now going on. The new views of geology tell us that this theory of uniformity is quite inadequate; and these new views say that the evidence, taken as a whole, points to some great world catastrophe, a real cataclysm, as having taken place in the long ago. And it says that if this great world-convulsion be regarded as an actual scientific or historical fact, we can then account for essentially all the great outstanding problems presented by the stratified rocks and their fossil contents. We may now consider briefly some of the facts which are relied upon to bring us to this conclusion.

III

A good example to begin with would be the fossil mammoths or elephants which have been found in Northern Siberia. Most people have read of these huge creatures which have been kept in natural cold storage for so many thousands of years, their flesh so well preserved that it is readily eaten by polar bears, wolves and dogs. But many are not aware of the enormous numbers of these creatures which are found in these arctic lands. Just when they were first discovered is not known; but ever since the tenth century at least, there has been a regular trade in the tusks of these fossil elephants, this trade going both eastward to China and westward to Europe, with a regular market quotation of price current for this fossil ivory, just as for wheat or cotton. There is an annual ivory sale in London; and while the figures are not at hand for recent years, in the year 1872 it is recorded that 1,630 tusks of Siberian mammoths were placed on sale, though the next year only 1,140 were reported. One author estimates that the tusks of a thousand animals are brought to market annually; while still another writer in a recent English magazine says that in one year he himself saw a thousand tusks. And since less than fifty per cent of the tusks actually found are in a state of preservation sufficient to warrant their being taken to these far-distant markets, one can have some idea of the enormous number of these animals which must have been discovered in the past hundreds or perhaps thousands of years.

The localities where they are found most frequently are also remarkable. Mammoth remains are scarce in Southern or Middle Siberia; but they abound in the extreme north, along the shore from the mouth of the

Obi to Bering Strait. They are more frequently found in the banks of the streams or rivers, or where the ocean has undermined the cliffs on the shore. It seems that they become increasingly abundant the further north we proceed, the islands of New Siberia, far within the Arctic Circle, being one of the chief collecting localities. Indeed, the soil of Bear Island and of the Liachoff Islands is reported to be composed almost as fully of mammoth bones as of sand and ice.

Under the extreme climate of these northern lands the soil remains continuously frozen to a depth of several hundred feet, thawing out only to a depth of a foot or two in favoured localities during the short summer, thus allowing for the growth of a few wild flowers and bushes. Most of the specimens of fossil elephants which have been described by competent scientists have been found when undermined by some stream, a part of the animal appearing in a certain season, next year a little more becoming visible, and the whole carcass having become loosened and having dropped to the bed of the stream only after several years of such gradual exposure. In this way, when finally loosened from the cliffs, the body is usually much decayed. But even under such conditions, the meat has sometimes been found so fresh as actually to be used for breakfast by the explorers who happened to make the discovery.

These fossil " mummies " are not found in clear ice, as is commonly supposed, but usually in stratified beds of sand or gravel intercalated with beds of clay, all of the beds being continuous and undisturbed, proving that they were buried in these beds as a natural deposit, and that the bodies of these animals had not fallen into some fissure in the strata. It very frequently happens that the animals appear to be in a semi-erect position; and thus when uncovered by the erosion of the surface, the tusks and the head are the first to appear. Not many specimens have been carefully reported on by competent scientists; but it seems to be the ordinary thing to find the animals with their stomachs well filled with undigested food; while the blood vessels of the head are congested with blood, as in the case of animals suffocated by drowning. One specimen at least is reported not only with a stomach full of food, but with its mouth full also, showing as one author expresses it, that the animal was " quietly feeding when the crisis came."

The modern Indian elephant is so nearly identical with these fossil mammoths that there can be no doubt they are of the same origin, even if we do not suppose the modern ones to be the direct descendants of the mammoths; for several other " species " of fossil elephants are also found in various parts of the northern hemisphere. But the modern elephants are entirely confined to the tropics, and whenever they have been taken to cooler countries they seem always to have had a hard time. History records that Hannibal brought thirty-seven elephants into Italy, but that only one of these had survived the first winter, when Hannibal undertook to cross the Arno. The suggestion that the elephant might possibly live in the present climate of Northern Siberia, seems too grotesque even to be mentioned here, if it had not been proposed by some people in an effort to evade the force of the argument presented by these elephants in cold storage.

The idea has been industriously circulated that these mammoths had a good coat of hair; and it has been argued from this that they may have been able to endure a cold climate. However, from the specimen of mammoth skin, a square foot or so in area, preserved in the National Museum at Washington, D. C., it will be seen that the hair, while long, is very thin, and could not have been of much protection against the cold. Recently, however, the skin of the mammoth has been subjected to a careful microscopic study; and it has been found that the skin, like that of the modern elephant, had neither sweat glands nor sebaceous glands, a peculiarity confined to a few animals which live wholly in the tropics. M. H. Neuville, to whom I am indebted for these facts, goes on to say:

"The very peculiar fur of the mammoth thus furnished only a precarious protection against cold, a protection analogous to that enjoyed at present by a few mammals of the tropical zone. Its dermis was, it is true, very thick, but no more so than that of existing elephants. It appears to me impossible to find in the anatomical examination of the skin and pelage, any argument in favour of adaptation to cold." (*Report of the Smithsonian Inst.*, 1919; p. 332.)

Not many scientists have ever attempted to explain these fossil "mummies" without some sudden and extensive change of climate. Thus, James D. Dana, the Nestor among the geologists of a generation ago, after speaking of the conclusive evidence of a warm, genial climate in these extreme arctic regions while the mammoth and his companion animals were living there, said that this wonderful climate must have been "abruptly terminated," and must have "become suddenly extreme as of a single winter's night," since which time it has never relaxed its arctic severity. Other scientists have used somewhat similar language, for these thousands of carcasses now found in such excellent cold storage are indubitable proofs of these facts.

But what was it that caused this sudden and extreme change of climate? Quite evidently this change of climate, whatever its cause, was associated with whatever buried these animals. But we are not prepared to assign a cause for these facts until we have considered several other groups of facts from other parts of the world. In other words, we need a general understanding of the causes which produced the geological changes as a whole; but the facts which we have been examining do not tend to increase our confidence in the theory of uniformity.

With some people who have not a full acquaintance with the facts, the popular notion of a " glacial age " comes in here as a possible explanation. But this myth of a great ice-cap covering most of North America and most of Europe, has been effectively disposed of by Sir Henry H. Howorth, in his three monumental works, the first of which, *The Mammoth and the Flood,* deals with the specific problem which we are here considering.

One more fact needs attention in this connection. Sir Samuel Baker, the noted African explorer, tells us that the body of an elephant when killed in the water does not sink to the bottom, but from the first the body floats with sufficient buoyancy to support two men or more. In contrast with this fact, the bodies of all other animals, so far as we are aware, sink to the bottom of the water, and only after decomposition has set in, a period varying from a few hours to several days, will the body rise to the surface because of its being distended with gases. But the body of the elephant will float on water from the very first. Accordingly, if we may suppose that a great aqueous convulsion was the prime cause of the destruction of all these animals, it is evident that the bodies of the elephants would remain floating on the surface; and then if a marked falling of temperature accompanied this flood of waters, these bodies of the elephants, or at least many of them, would be found frozen in the surface ice, and if the latter were subsequently buried, the bodies of these elephants would also share the same fate and be covered by beds of sand or gravel.

IV

Another good example for study in this connection would be the fossil fishes. In many parts of the world, as in the Green River shales of Wyoming; the Lompoc beds, near Santa Barbara, California; the black shales of Glarus, Switzerland; or those of Monte Bolca, Italy; or of Solenhofen, Germany; large areas are found with the rocks packed full of fishes in a remarkable condition of preservation. Not only is the full outline of the fishes preserved, but even the soft parts are exquisitely shown, thus giving proof that these animals were buried alive, or at least before decomposition had set in. Nothing but some extraordinary convulsion of nature is adequate to explain the facts as we find them.

As is well known, the Devonian rocks were formerly known as the Old Red Sandstone. These strata, found in almost all parts of the world, are so characterized by the remains of vertebrate fishes that they were often assigned to an " Age of Fishes," by the evolutionary geologists of a century ago. Hugh Miller has given us a very picturesque account of the fossils of the Devonian as they occur in various parts of Scotland, and after saying that the condition in which these fossils are found presents us with " a wonderful record of violent death falling at once, not on a few individuals, but on whole tribes," he says that " some terrible catastrophe involved in sudden destruction the fish of an area at least a hundred miles from boundary to boundary, perhaps much more." And he asks, " By what quiet but potent agency of destruction were the innumerable existences of an area perhaps ten thousand square miles in extent annihilated at once? "

In many places in America as well as in Europe, where remains of fishes are found in such enormous numbers, the shale or slate is so saturated with oil that the rock will burn almost like coal. Indeed, Prof. J. M. MacFarlane, of the University of Pennsylvania, has recently issued a book, entitled *Fishes the Source of Petroleum,* (1923), in which he argues that these fish remains are the chief if not the sole source of our mineral oils. Formerly it was thought that these extraordinary beds of fish were confined largely to the Devonian. In a similar way it used to be thought that the coal beds were confined to what was termed the Carboniferous. But it is now known that coal beds occur in every one of the formations from the Devonian onwards; and in the same way it is now known that these great accumulations of fishes are also found in every single one of the formations from the Silurian to the Tertiary. We have already shown that these names of the geologic systems *have no chronological value,* but are simply convenient names for classification purposes. From all this we learn that these telltale fish deposits occur in all parts of the globe and in almost all of the various formations. The evolutionary geologist would have these deposits formed by many separate catastrophes; but it would be more scientific and more logical to suppose that they are all instances of what happened during that great world catastrophe which seems to be the clear and unequivocal testimony of the rocks in all parts of the globe. And if our petroleum deposits were produced by these buried fish remains, we can judge of the enormous quantities of fish which must have been buried at this time.

In this book by Professor MacFarlane, which was published by the Macmillan Co. only last year (1923), we have an unusually clear and forceful argument to prove that fishes, buried in uncounted millions and in some sudden and catastrophic manner in each particular instance, must have furnished the organic materials from which by chemical change our immense petroleum deposits have been produced. We have space here to quote only a sentence or two from the summary of his argument. Thus he says:

"In review of the evidence presented in preceding chapters, the author is compelled to accept that fishes are the source of practically the entire supply of crude petroleum, also of natural petroleum derivatives like the asphaltites. For fishes alone meet the requirements of the case" (p. 384).

Or again:

"It can be definitely said that, through all of the geologic formations in which fish remains occur, a large proportion of the remains consist of entire fishes or of sections in which every scale is still in position; every fin is extended as in life attitude; the bones of the head, though often crushed in and broken through subsequent diastrophic strains, still retain almost the normal positions; while near them may be coprolites of the same or some other types of fish in a practically entire state. All of this conclusively proves that when myriads of such fishes were simultaneously killed, their bodies were deposited or stranded within a few hours or a few days at most after death, so that the flesh, the liver, the alimentary canal and other soft parts were unquestionably enclosed and intact, when sediment sealed them up. For numerous experiments that the writer has undertaken prove, that even after five to six days dead fishes begin to lose scales, to be attacked and nibbled at by other fishes, by crabs, and by smaller fry, while as yet the flesh and entrails are enclosed, though softened. We unhesitatingly conclude then that a large proportion of the fishes met with in 'fish beds' and oil strata were stretched out and preserved intact either immediately or within a day or two at most after death" (p. 400).

De la Beche, the first Director of the Geological Survey of Great Britain, was quite positive in stating that not only the fishes but also most of the larger animals must have been buried suddenly in a very abnormal manner. "A very large proportion of them," he declares, "must have been entombed uninjured, and many alive, or, if not alive, at least before decomposition ensued" (*Theoretical Geology*, p. 265, London, 1834). And in this language this accomplished geologist is speaking not of the fishes alone, but of the fossiliferous deposits in general.

V

If we turn to the invertebrates, we find the same tell-tale evidence from the fossils that they were buried in some extraordinary way. In millions of instances the two valves of pelecypod mollusks are found applied, with the interior of the shells empty, thus proving that these shells had not been washed about by the currents after the animals had died; for these shells tend to gape or open just as soon as the animal dies. The brachiopods are also usually found with the shells empty, though there is a small hole in the hinge region of these shells which would admit mud if the shell is subjected to washing by currents of water after the animal is dead. When these valves are found closed and the interior hollow it is proof that the death of the animals and their burial was probably sudden. Further evidence in this direction is found in the fact that our modern brachiopods are mostly found in the deep waters only, where there are absolutely no currents under the normal or modern condition.

Indeed, the burial of these deep-sea animals in well-stratified beds, often mixed up with other animals derived from the lands, or still more often interbedded with sandstones or other deposits clearly derived from the land, is clear proof that somehow the normal conditions of land and water must have been greatly disturbed. For in the depths of the ocean there are now no currents whatever, no movement of the waters to disturb the most fragile oozes which now cover all of the ocean bottom. Accordingly, nothing but a veritable convulsion of nature could interbed these deposits from the bottom of the ocean with those sands and gravels which are solely the products of land erosion.

VI

These abnormal conditions are capable of endless illustration from the rocks. The strata of almost every mountain range on earth contain plenty of evidence of these abnormal conditions. In my *Fundamentals of Geology,* and also in my *New Geology,* I have considered this subject at considerable length. To these works the reader must be referred for further details. Here it may suffice to say that the concurrent testimony of the geological deposits throughout the world is that *some very profound and very enormous catastrophe must have happened to our world sometime in the long ago*. The cumulative evidence on this point can no longer be ignored or denied. That some great world-convulsion must have taken place *since man and the other living species of plants and animals were alive*, is as well established an historical event as is the destruction of Carthage or the fall of Babylon. And any scheme of organic evolution which *ignores* this great world event is simply building upon the sands. No such scheme has the slightest scientific value for the world as a whole, if it goes on absolutely ignoring this clearly demonstrated fact. Every theory regarding the changes which may have taken place in the structures and instincts of animals and plants, must make a full allowance for this great world-event, the most stupendous physical fact within the direct scope of human knowledge. Accordingly, due allowance must be made for the consequences of this great event in any system of biology or of organic philosophy which expects to build permanently upon facts.

VII

Let us take some more specific examples. And let us consider the largest creatures which ever walked the earth, the dinosaurs. "One of the most inexplicable of events," remarks R. S. Lull of these creatures, "is the dramatic extinction of this mighty race." He means that there is no well established reason for their extinction at all, least of all for their apparent *simultaneous extinction over the whole world*. This is what makes their extinction so "dramatic;" for we must remember that these great creatures were not by any means confined to North America, but also lived in Europe, in East Africa, and throughout the central part of Asia, perhaps also elsewhere. And Henry Fairfield Osborn declares that " The cutting off of this giant dinosaur dynasty was nearly if not quite simultaneous the world over." Dr. Lull was making no chance remark when he called the extinction of this mighty race " dramatic."

But we have already seen that many other extinctions of races were probably very dramatic. If we take the elephants and their companion Pleistocene mammals which used to live in North America, it is impossible to avoid the conviction that they were killed off by some most extraordinary physical event. As Dr. O. P. Hay remarks, the animals found in the Pleistocene strata of North America include the great ground sloths, the glyptodons, many species of horses, several tapirs, numerous kinds of giant pigs, camels, the extinct relatives of the musk-oxen, extinct bisons, many elephants, mastodons of three or four genera, the giant beaver, and the sabertooth tiger. As this author remarks, " Genera and families, even orders, were wiped out of existence, and these included some of the noblest animals that have graced the face of the earth." (*The Pleistocene of North America and its Vertebrated Animals*, p. 5; Carnegie Institution; 1923.)

But when we further remember that the long popular method of arranging the fossils off in an alleged chronological order is now known to have been a big blunder, it is very evident that we have a most astonishing collection of fossils which must very generally have been killed off and buried by flowing water in some most extraordinary way. If the fishes were very generally throughout the world killed in such millions as to be the chief if not the sole source of our great petroleum deposits, if the dinosaurs were probably contemporary with the gigantic mammals of the Pleistocene, and if the shellfish and other invertebrates also present us with similar evidences of having been suddenly overwhelmed, surely we have a most complete vindication of the record of that most stupendous of physical events, the Deluge of the Scriptures. "The world that then was, being overflowed with water, perished."

Noah's Flood

VIII

One of the most complete statements of the arguments for organic evolution is a book, entitled *Readings in Evolution, Genetics, and Eugenics,* by Dr. H. H. Newman, of the University of Chicago. It is a sort of extended scrap-book made up of elaborate extracts from the classical evolutionary writers, with many comments of the editor. Dr. Newman gives the usual arguments based on the fossils of the horse, the elephants, and the camels which have been arranged in an alleged historical order in many of the great museums. But he undertakes to summarize the geological evidence for organic evolution in ten statements (pp. 69, 70). Of these ten facts, not one is absolutely and unqualifiedly true; while some of them are perfectly grotesque as summaries of the facts now known from the rocks. I need not discuss these ten points in detail here. Suffice it to say that these statements are antiquated, they exhibit a begging of the main question in almost every instance, and are wholly misleading and deceptive as a statement of the facts of geology which bear on the problem of organic evolution. But presumably they were the best Dr. Newman could do.

For the details of the geological argument I must refer the reader again to my other works, particularly to my more recent one, *The New Geology, a Textbook for Colleges* (1923). But in view of the utter collapse of the chronological distinctions between the various fossils which have been so long relied upon by evolutionists, I do not think that the well-informed reader can have any profound faith still remaining in the line of evidence for evolution based on geology. And yet we should bear in mind that no less an authority than Thomas Hunt Morgan has told us that " The direct evidence furnished by fossil remains is by all odds the strongest evidence that we have in favour of organic evolution " (*Critique*, p. 24).

IX

Ere closing this chapter we should note again the almost complete despair among the modern botanists regarding the tracing out of the lines of evolution among the great groups of plants. The present situation among the students of botany may be illustrated by the latest work of D. H. Scott, *Extinct Plants and Problems of Evolution* (1924). No one can read this work, together with the recent declarations of such men as H. B. Guppy, A. G. Tansley, and A. C. Seward, without feeling that these men are about giving up any hope of being able to strengthen the argument for organic evolution by any study of the evidence furnished by fossil botany. This subject is too large a one to present here in detail, though a few representative quotations may not be amiss.

In 1916, Dr. J. P. Lotsy had declared: " Phylogeny, *i. e.* reconstruction of what has happened in the past, is no science, but a product of fantastic speculations " (*Evolution by Means of Hybridization*, p. 140).

Scott thinks that this may be going a little too far; but he says, " Like Dr. Lotsy, I have become skeptical of late as to most phylogenetic reconstructions " (*Extinct Plants*, p. 18).

He proceeds to say:

" The evolution of plants, so far as the record shows, does not present a uniform progression, but rather a series of diverse periods of vegetation, each with a character of its own " (p. 215).

Exactly so; these diverse groups of vegetation, " each with a character of its own," are merely the buried floras of the ancient world, and undoubtedly all lived contemporary with each other. It was only by a confusion of thought that the early geological explorers thought they could place the various geological " formations " in different ages and could arrange them in a real chronological order, though these formations have had to be made up from scattered localities all over the world. And it is by the perpetuation of this blunder that most people still seem to think there really must be some reality to the long-drawn-out chronological arrangement of these scattered floras and faunas, as taught us these many decades by evolutionary geology.[1]   The zoologists have had things

---

[1] NOTE.—The finding of a large one-toed horse's foot, well carbonized, in a coal bed of the Laramie (Cretaceous) formation at Scofield, Utah, is like many other similar discoveries which have been constantly occurring during the entire history of geological investigations.   It is discredited because

pretty much their own way, and have been able to present their little artificially arranged series of animals in such a way as to make these animals " present a uniform progression " very nicely; but the botanists have not been much consulted in the serial arrangement of the geological formations, and so now we hear them complain that their fossil plants do not " present a uniform progression," as Scott expresses it.

He tells us some of the ways in which the great groups of plants do " not present a uniform progression ":

" The record [geological series] shows no time-limit between Monocotyledons and Dicotyledons, and throws no light on the possible derivation of the one class from the other. Both extend back far into the Cretaceous, and throughout the whole time the Dicotyledons appear more numerous than the Monocotyledons, as they are at the present day " (p. 43).

The large and important group of Pteridosperms, with the habit of Ferns but bearing highly organized seeds on their fronds, have seemed to the evolutionists a promising half-way stage between the true ferns and the true seed-plants. But Scott tells us that this arrangement cannot be made to work. For:

it is so contrary to the prevailing theories. The finding of an angiosperm stem in a coal-ball of the Carboniferous of Harrisburg, Illinois, is almost equally disconcerting to the evolutionary theories; but it has been announced in an " orthodox " scientific manner (Dr. A. C. Noe, " A Paleozoic Angiosperm," *Journal of Geology,* May-June, 1923, pp. 344-347), and accordingly must now be regarded as " authentic." But all such discoveries only tend to prove *that a fossil is not necessarily old because it is found in a Cambrian or an Ordovician bed, and another fossil is not necessarily young because it is found in a Tertiary deposit.*

" On a review of the whole evidence, the former belief in the origin of the Pteridosperms (and through them of the Seed-plants generally) from Ferns must be given up. There is no reason to believe that Ferns, as botanists understand the name, are any older than the Pteridosperms themselves; the points in common between the two groups now appear to be homoplastic, and not indicative of the descent of the one from the other. Thus the origin of the Seed-plants is still an unsolved problem " (pp. 207-8).

" On the whole, one is impressed with the independence of the various phyla of vascular plants all through the geological record " (p. 202).

Evidently there is not much encouragement to evolutionary speculations here. Even when they have had the world to pick from, and have been able (except for the predominating influence of the zoologists) to arrange the various scattered " formations " according to their liking, the botanists have not been able to make their fossil plants " present a uniform progression." It is really too bad.

X

The fact is, geology furnishes no true evidence for the theory of organic evolution. On the contrary, if we look at the fossil world in a broad way, it is impossible to avoid the conviction of a catastrophic death and burial of the vast majority of the animals and plants found as fossils in the strata. Lyell and his followers have always tried to blunt the force of this evidence by formulating an alleged chronological scheme of the geological deposits all over the globe, so as to have these burials take place a few at a time, on a sort of instalment plan. But the methods employed to formulate this alleged chronology have always been regarded by the keenest and most logical thinkers as a burlesque on true scientific methods; and as I have shown in my special works on this subject, these methods must be abandoned, and a truer and more scientific theory of the science must be allowed to give us the bare facts, without their being overlaid so completely by evolutionary theory. A true and impartial science of geology tells us of *the ruins of a world, not of its growth and development*.

The voluminous materials which have so long been taught to the world under the name of geology, constitute a vast mixture of facts and grotesque speculations; and the average student of this science has hitherto been quite unable to discriminate between the statements made in the name of this science, and tell how much is real fact and how much is only mere hypothesis or theory. But this differentiation is now beginning to be made. And it is now becoming very evident that, if the mere speculative parts of geology be cast aside, there are no real indisputable facts regarding the rocks or the fossils which could not be readily accounted for by the hypothesis of a world-cataclysm. Accordingly, this hypothesis now stands before the world as at least a possible explanation of the facts, and indeed as much the most reasonable explanation of these facts.

But all this is fully in accord with that sublime record of the early days of our earth, which tells us that the world " that then was, being overflowed with water, perished."

And if this record be taken at its face value, either from nature or from revelation, the theory of organic evolution becomes indeed a phantom.

BIBLIOGRAPHY

Geikie, Sir A., *The Founders of Geology;* 1901.

Grabau, A. W., *Principles of Stratigraphy;* 1913.
           Textbook of Geology; 1920.

Hay, O. P., *The Pleistocene of North America;* 1923.

Howorth, Sir H. H., *The Mammoth and the Flood;* 1887.
           The Glacial Nightmare and the Flood,
           2 vols.; 1892.
           Ice or Water, 2 vols.; 1905.

(These works of Howorth are an effectual refutation of
the Glacial Theory. They have never been answered.)

MacFarlane, J. M., *Fishes the Source of Petroleum;* 1923.

Pirsson, L. V., and Schuchert, Chas., *Textbook of Geology;*
1920.

Price, Geo. McCready, *The Fundamentals of Geology;* 1913.
           *The Fossils as Age-Markers in Geol-
           ogy; Princeton Theological Re-
           view,* October, 1922.
           *The New Geology, a Textbook for
           Colleges;* 1923.
           *Geology and Its Relation to Scrip-
           ture Revelation; Transactions of
           the Victoria Institute;* 1924.

Scott, D. H., *Extinct Plants and Problems of Evolution;* 1924.

Willis, Bailey, and Salisbury, R. D., *Outlines of Geologic
History;* 1912.

Zittel, K., *History of Geology and Paleontology;* 1901.

IV

FOLLOWING THE GLEAM

I

THERE was a time, during the latter part of the nineteenth century, when the evolution theory seemed a very plausible or even a probable explanation of the origin of our various plants and animals. At that time the world in general believed in the historical value of the arrangement of the fossil plants and animals as then almost universally accepted by geologists. Charles Darwin accepted this geological series as a true chronological outline of the order in which the various plants and animals had appeared on earth; and his argument was that it was more reasonable to suppose that the higher forms (alleged by the geologists to be *later* in point of time) had developed naturally out of the lower forms (alleged to have preceded them), than to suppose a great many successive creations of new kinds to have been perpetually going on during the past history of the world. And he undertook to show how the change from one species to another might have been brought about by gradual processes similar to processes now prevailing in our modern world.

This was a very reasonable suggestion on Darwin's part; and when he adduced so many illustrative examples, and seemed to give a plausible account of how one " species " might become transformed over into another and distinctly different kind of animal or plant, the world accepted his apparent demonstration of the " origin of species " as a proof of the larger doctrine of general organic evolution. But in our day, with the total breakdown of the geological argument, we are now in the singular position of believing in the " origin of species," in the narrower meaning of this term, and yet denying *in toto* the general theory of the development of the higher forms of animals and plants from the lower forms.

II

It may be well for us here to consider briefly the rise of the doctrine of evolution.

This doctrine is not of a modern origin. It dates from the days of the early Greeks, who, well acquainted with the teeming sea-life of the waters of the blue Ægean, invented novel hypotheses as to the origin of the various kinds of plants and animals. Thales (624-548 B. C.) was perhaps the first of the Greeks to theorize about the origin of life. Anaximander, his contemporary, taught a gradual evolution of the land animals, including man, from certain aquatic species. Various other speculators followed up these ideas, until in Empedocles (495-435 B. C.) we have one who, Osborn tells us, " may justly be called the father of the evolution idea." Like all consistent evolutionists, he believed in *abiogenesis,* or spontaneous generation, as the explanation of the origin of life. He taught that the development of life was a gradual process; that plants were evolved before animals; that imperfect forms became extinct, and were gradually replaced by more perfect forms.

" With Aristotle (384-322 B. C.) we enter a new

world," says Osborn. "He towered above his predecessors, and by the force of his genius created natural history." His knowledge of nature was encyclopedic; and while his ideas were somewhat vague, he taught many things which are now incorporated in our modern evolution doctrine. He rejected the materialistic theories of some of his predecessors, such as Empedocles, and favoured the idea of intelligent design in nature. But he believed in the gradual development of the higher forms of life, including man, from the lower and less highly organized. Aristotle is the originator of the persistent fallacy known as "prenatal influences," and he taught very positively the inheritance of acquired characters.

The influence of Aristotle over the philosophy and the science of subsequent centuries was so profound that many of the early church fathers incorporated some of the prime ideas of the evolution doctrine into their teachings. Thus, Gregory of Nyssa (331-396 A. D.) taught that creation was merely potential. God imparted to matter certain properties, and thereafter matter developed in accordance with the laws thus established. Augustine (353-430 A. D.) suggested the idea, now so widely accepted, that the Biblical account of creation is to be understood as an allegory. He said: "In the beginning God made the heaven and the earth, as if this were the seed of the heaven and the earth, although as yet all the matter of heaven and of earth was in confusion, but because it was certain that from this the heaven and the earth would be, therefore the material itself is called by that name." Thus we see that Augustine brought over into Christian theology the old heathen idea of a primitive chaos; but he also used language which might well accord with the doctrine of a gradual development or evolution.

Thomas Aquinas (1225-74), one of the greatest philosophers of the Middle Ages, copied after the teachings of Augustine, and claimed that in the first production of plants, the grass and trees were merely brought forth *causaliter;* that is, the earth " then received the power to produce them." Thus the real idea of a direct creation was obscured, and according to this philosophy the evolution doctrine might be reconciled with the account of creation as given in the first chapter of Genesis.

III

With the revival of the study of natural science, many speculators indulged their fancies in explanation of the curious forms of life found as fossils in the rocks. Some of these early geologists supposed that there had been long ages of development, in which the earth had passed through successive changes of land and water. Others said that the fossils were mere sports of nature; and that their resemblance to modern animals and plants was merely a curious coincidence. Others, however, like Leonardo da Vinci (1452-1519), the celebrated painter, and John Woodward (1665-1722), the English naturalist, taught that the fossils represent real plants and animals which formerly lived on the earth. This part of the history shows how tenaciously the real meaning of the fossils was contested.

Along with these speculations in geology there were many similar fantastic views put forth by students of living plants and animals.

During the eighteenth century the natural sciences

became more generally studied, and the foundations of modern science were then laid.

Linnaeus (1707-78) was the originator of the system of classification still prevailing in botany and zoology, and the inventor of our present system of binomial nomenclature for both plants and animals. He was an advocate of the doctrine of special creation, holding that all of the distinct species which we have to-day are similar to the kinds originally created; though he made allowance for new combinations of species which may have arisen through hybridization or through degeneration. He was the greatest naturalist of his day, and his influence was strongly against any form of the evolution idea.

Buffon (1707-88) may be called the father of the modern form of the evolution doctrine. He was much more of a speculator than a true scientist, a man " whose genius, unballasted by an adequate knowledge of facts, often played him sad tricks " (Marcus Hartog). The chief idea which he contributed to the growing doctrine of organic evolution, was that the direct influence of the environment brings about a modification in the structure of plants and animals, and that these modifications of structure are passed along through heredity. In geology, too, his fanciful speculations gave rise to the doctrine of seven successive " epochs," in which he professed to picture not only the beginning and the past of our planet, but also its future. In view of his own fantastic speculations, it seems singular that he should reproach the geologists of his day with resembling the ancient Roman augurs who could not meet each other without laughing at the frauds which they were all in the habit of perpetrating upon the common people.

Modern evolutionists, however, find many things to object to in Buffon's zoology. He taught that the modern pig could not have been created on any complete and perfect plan originally, but must have been constructed as a compound from other animals, since, he declared, it has many useless parts. He also taught that " the ass is a degenerate horse, and the ape a degenerate man " (Osborn).

Erasmus Darwin (1731-1802) was a physician, an amateur naturalist, and took himself quite seriously as a poet. He was the grandfather of Charles Darwin, and undoubtedly the latter received many of his ideas from Erasmus, who left considerable writings which strongly advocated an evolutionary origin for the plants and animals. " Erasmus Darwin derived the idea of generation rather than the creation of the world from David Hume " (R. H. Lock, *Variation, Heredity and Evolution,* p. 29). His theory of how organic evolution takes place was very similar to that of Lamarck, who was living contemporaneously in France; but it seems that the two men had no knowledge of each other. Erasmus Darwin dwelt on the changes brought about by the exertions of animals in response to their desires and physical pains or pleasures, and he taught that many of these newly acquired changes of structure or changes of instinct are transmitted to their descendants. By the cumulative effect of these changes great transformations could be brought about after many millions of years. Indeed, his own language was that these processes had been going on " perhaps millions of ages before the commencement of the history of mankind," and that these improvements may continue to go on from generation to generation " world without end." In view of these teachings, it is quite inaccurate to speak of Charles Darwin as having been in any sense the originator of the doctrine of organic evolution.

IV

Lamarck (1744-1829), the French naturalist, is often spoken of as the founder of the complete theory of organic evolution in its modern form. " The stigma placed upon his writings by Cuvier, who greeted every fresh edition of his works as a *nouvelle folie,* and the disdainful allusions to him by Charles Darwin (the only writer of whom Darwin ever spoke in this tone) long placed him in the light of a purely extravagant, speculative thinker. Yet, as a fresh instance of the certainty with which men of science finally obtain recognition, it is gratifying to note the admiration which has been accorded to him in Germany by Haeckel and others, by his countrymen, and by a large school of American and English writers of the present day; to note, further, that his theory was finally taken up and defended by Charles Darwin himself, and that it forms the very heart of the system of Herbert Spencer." (Osborn.)

Lamarck is usually considered the originator of the idea that acquired characters are transmitted to the next generation, and this idea is now spoken of as the " Lamarckian doctrine." Among the factors which he considered as playing an important role in the evolution of plants and animals, were the favourable changes in environment, new physical wants or necessities, the effects of use and disuse, the effects of competition, the effects of cross-breeding, and the alleged fact that the changes induced in any of these ways are passed along in heredity to the next generation.

Modern evolutionists, such as Osborn, admit that in his philosophical writings upon evolution Lamarck's " speculations far outran his observations, and his theory suffered from the absurd illustrations which he brought forward in his support of it. . . . His critics spread the impression that he believed animals acquired new organs simply by wishing for them." It is also admitted that his speculations in zoology were subject to discredit and injury " by his earlier thoroughly worthless speculation in chemistry and other branches of science " (Osborn). In fact, he had so little philosophical insight that he " left wholly untouched and unsolved " many problems connected with the origin of adaptations. " His arguments are, in most cases, not inductive, but deductive, and are frequently found not to support his law but to postulate it " (Osborn). In short, Lamarck did not show any of that careful adherence to proved facts which is rightly regarded as the prime characteristic of a true scientist. But he lived in a day when it was fashionable to discredit the Christian religion, and he sought to give an apparent scientific foundation for this disbelief.

V

Georges Cuvier (1769-1832) was the foremost scientist and naturalist of his day. He was in many respects a very extraordinary man, and was not only an opponent of Lamarck, but of organic evolution in general. Indeed, his wonderful scientific attainments and his strong personality so dominated the scientific thought of his day that the ideas of evolution then struggling for recognition became quite discredited. Particularly was this the case in the controversy between Cuvier and Geoffroy St. Hilaire (1772-1844), a thoroughgoing evolutionist, who defended the doctrine of Buffon, that the direct action of the environment is the real cause of evolution. This controversy came to a climax in the year 1830, and left Cuvier completely master of the field; and for several decades thereafter the theory of organic evolution " sank into oblivion," as August Weismann expresses it, " and was expunged from the pages of science so completely that it seemed as if it were forever buried beyond hope of resurrection." Indeed, this condition prevailed down until the publication of *The Origin of Species*, in 1859.

Unfortunately, in spite of his determined opposition to any speculations regarding organic evolution, Baron Cuvier was in reality laying more securely the real foundation for the subsequent revival of this doctrine. This he did by his theories of geology. He had made himself familiar with the fossils found in the strata around Paris, and he conceived the idea that it would be a splendid thing to be able to trace out the chronological relationship between the various groups of life.

" How glorious," he declared, " it would be if we could arrange the organized products of the universe in their chronological order, as we can already [referring here to Werner's onion-coats] do with the more important mineral substances."

By the year 1808 Cuvier with several assistants had arranged the strata around Paris in what he conceived to be a strict chronological order. Unconscious of the futility of making this little district the measure for the entire world, and unaware of the fact that he was perpetuating on the scientific world an organic onion-coat theory just as absurd as that taught by A. G.

Werner, Cuvier built up an entire scheme of organic creation, in which he had over a dozen successive cataclysms which swept over the world and piled up the beds of fossiliferous strata. He was a Lutheran in religion, and acted as superintendent of the faculty of Protestant theology in the University of Paris. And of course, in having so many successive cataclysms, which he said destroyed all living things on earth, he had to have a corresponding number of successive creations, in order to start the world over again each time. He made the flood of Noah the last of this series; though in this cataclysm not all of the preceding kinds of life were wholly annihilated.

This theory of "catastrophism," as it is usually called, really laid broad and secure the foundation for that great superstructure of evolutionary theory which in our day has so captured the imagination of the world. It was a system of arranging the fossils from all of the globe in an alleged chronological order, this order in its general outline representing a steady advance from the lower and less organized types of life to the higher and more specially organized; and the geologists of the subsequent hundred years have been chiefly employed in filling in the details of this outline. Lyell's work was to smooth out the connections between these successive events; he denied the reality of these successive catastrophes or cataclasms, and said that all of the geological changes took place by slow imperceptible gradations, quite in accord with the orderly behaviour of nature in our modern world. And Darwin's work merely put the finishing touches to the doctrine, by showing how the various kinds of plants or animals were probably transformed into other distinctly different kinds by the similar operation of laws and processes alleged to be now going on. *Thus by the combined work of Lyell and Darwin a system of uniformity, both inorganic and organic, replaced the system of catastrophism advocated by Cuvier.* But Darwin could never have had a half dozen people to listen to him if Cuvier and Lyell had not acted as his advance agents in preparing the way for his views.

VI

Charles Lyell (1797-1875), by his system of uniformitarian geology, was, as Huxley declared, "the chief agent in smoothing the road for Darwin. For consistent uniformitarianism postulates evolution as much in the organic as in the inorganic world" (*Life and Letters,* Vol. 1, p. 168). When Darwin as a young man started out on his historic voyage on the *Beagle,* he took with him a copy of Lyell's *Principles of Geology,* then only lately published. On this trip he read this work with great admiration, and in publishing the journal of this voyage some years afterwards he dedicated it to Charles Lyell.

The influence on Darwin's mind of the work of Malthus *On Population,* which has often been mentioned as one of the inciting causes of Darwin's invention of the theory of natural selection, has been much exaggerated. Doubtless it was an inciting cause of this immediate theory; but it was merely like the match which sets off the gunpowder, for some such theory of organic evolution was inevitable, in view of the system of geology then universally taught.

Charles Darwin (1809-82), after studying medicine at Edinburgh, matriculated at Cambridge, as a candidate for the church. But he had a strong liking for the various branches of natural science; and when

shortly after his graduation he was given an opportunity to join the ship *Beagle* as naturalist, in a voyage of exploration around the world, he accepted the
offer. Five years were spent in this way; but it was
not until many years after his return that he published
his first work in advocacy of the doctrine of evolution.

Alfred Russel Wallace (1822-1913) had read
Lyell's *Principles of Geology*, Malthus' *On Population*, and Robert Chamber's *Vestiges of Creation*,
which had appeared in 1844. Wallace was engaged in
collecting specimens in Borneo, when the idea of
natural selection occurred to him one day like an intui-
tion. He immediately wrote out a paper on the subject and sent it to Charles Darwin in England. Darwin had already been working along the same lines for
many years, but had not published anything on the
subject. The outcome of the matter was that a paper
prepared by Darwin was presented along with the
paper from Wallace before the Linnean Society on
July 1, 1858; and in November of the next year appeared Darwin's *Origin of Species*, with results which
are familiar to every one.

As already remarked, Darwin took for granted all
that the geologists were then teaching regarding the
precise order in which the various kinds of life had
appeared on the globe. He also took for granted that
plants and animals exhibit a constant tendency to vary
or change, in practically all directions and to an un-
measured or even an unlimited extent. He assumed
also that the changes in structure or in habits brought
about in one generation through any cause whatever
would be faithfully transmitted to the next generation.
But he placed the chief dependence of his theory upon
his own personal invention, namely, the theory of selec-

tion, both natural and sexual. The first effect of his *Origin of Species* was that it received the strong approval of many of his contemporary scientists. In course of time, however, scientists became impatient of this doctrine of the survival of the fittest, and began to ask, "What is the *origin* of the fittest?" That is, if we may suppose that organisms fitted to their environment are already in existence, we may well understand that such good adaptations will naturally survive; but how could these fittest forms *originate in the first place?* Even all the separate organs would seem to be similarly without explanation as to their origin; for until the fins of the fish, the wings of the bat, the legs of the quadruped, or the eyes of any creature on earth, were sufficiently developed to be *already useful* to their possessors, the laws of natural selection would tend inevitably to eliminate them instead of to perpetuate them. As it has been expressed by another, "natural selection may explain the survival of the fittest, but it cannot explain the arrival of the fittest."

A more complete discussion of the theory of natural selection will be presented in Chapter VIII of the present work.

But we must remember that in the days of Charles Darwin the science of embryology had already made considerable progress, and that the "recapitulation theory" of embryology, as it is usually called, was already well recognized, at least in its outline form, long before Darwin's *Origin of Species*. As it was taught in Darwin's day, this theory said that the embryo of one of the higher animals, such as man, passes in its development through all the lower stages of the animal kingdom, being successively a protozoon, a mollusk, a fish, a reptile, and a mammal. Crude as such an idea really was, it seemed to be in accord with the rude knowledge of embryology then prevailing; and it has taken over half a century of most painstaking observation and experiment to banish this theory to the limbo of discarded fancies, where the many blunders are preserved for the amusement of the students of the history of scientific speculations.

VII

It was Louis Agassiz (1807-1873), a brilliant pupil of the learned Cuvier, who became the most enthusiastic teacher of this idea of the embryo recapitulating or repeating all the series of types below it in the scale. He used it constantly in his own forceful and enthusiastic way for readjusting the classification of the living animals, by comparing the embryonic development of any particular type with the classification series adjusted to fit it; he also used this method for checking up and rearranging in a more truly " historical " order (so he said) the various fossils found in the rocks. Agassiz was the first to study living and fossil fishes in a comprehensive way; though after his masterly classification of the fishes he turned his attention to many other departments of the animal kingdom. But in his classification of such animals as the fishes he claimed that anatomical differences alone were not sufficient to furnish a basis for a complete classification. More and more as he progressed in his studies he depended upon the facts of embryology " to make good the deficiencies of fossil remains and to prevent the confusion " which he felt would result if the classification were to rest upon anatomical differences alone (Davidson, *The Recapitulation Theory,* p. 10). In his famous *Essay on Classification*, issued in 1857, or two years before the *Origin of Species*, Agassiz wrote, " I satisfied myself long ago that embryology furnishes the most trustworthy standard to determine the relative rank among animals."

Thus we see that Agassiz, with his method of comparing the embryonic development with the modern classification series and also with the geological series, had laid an apparently strong and deep foundation upon which subsequent biologists erected the gigantic structure of organic evolution. Le Conte, who was a great admirer of Agassiz, nevertheless blames the latter for not going the whole road with Darwin, Huxley, and Spencer; and indeed one can hardly see how Agassiz could logically have stopped where he did. Certain it is that his work, in elaborating the close similarity between the individual development of living animals, the geological succession (an artificial arrangement), and the relative rank or gradation of our living animals in a classification series (also an artificial arrangement), furnished one of the most compelling of all the arguments used by Romanes, Haeckel, and many others, as well as by Darwin himself, in establishing their theory of organic evolution.

VIII

Herbert Spencer (1820-1903) was one of the strong supporters of the general theory of evolution; but he depended chiefly upon the idea of the inheritance of acquired characters, the theory of Lamarck. On this subject he declared: " Close contemplation of the facts impresses me more strongly than ever with the two alternatives—either there has been inheritance of ac-

quired characters, or there has been no evolution"
(*Contemporary Review*, February-March, 1893).

Although Spencer fought a gradually losing battle
over this idea of the heritability of characters acquired
through the effects of environment or of use and disuse, he was one of the strongest advocates of the general doctrine of evolution from star mist to the mind
of man; and it was largely because of his vigourous
teaching of the doctrine that it gained the popularity
among the English speaking people which it now pos-
sesses. His theory of " physiological units " was probably what suggested Darwin's theory of " pangenesis,"
by which the latter undertook to explain how particular kinds of units are continually being given off from
every part of the body into the blood, thus making
a plausible account of the mechanics of heredity,—
though this theory has long since been discarded. But
Spencer's advocacy of the Neo-Lamarckian doctrine
was strongly opposed by August Weismann, an inci-
dent in the history of the idea which will be considered
presently.

IX

Thomas Henry Huxley (1825-1895) was a very
keen writer, and used to call himself " Darwin's bull-
dog;" while Darwin himself called Huxley " my general agent." Huxley accepted the theory of natural
selection always with considerable reservations; and
down even to the close of his life he insisted that Darwin's theory was not demonstrated. But he held
strongly to the general doctrine of organic evolution,
basing his central thought upon the supposed evidence
of paleontology, or the science of the fossils, as indeed
all clear thinkers have always done.

X

Ernst Haeckel (1834-1919) was one of the first men in Germany to accept the suggestions of Charles Darwin. He hailed Darwin's book as an " Anti-Genesis," and throughout his life he was engaged in a campaign to spread his philosophic theory of monistic materialism, and to support this theory chiefly by an appeal to the doctrine of organic evolution. Regarding his advocacy of the theory of natural selection, Professor H. H. Newman says that " beyond question, Haeckel over-applied the theory, and in a sense weakened its influence by his rather uncritical use of materials " (*Readings*, p. 30). This latter expression is rather a polite euphemism for what many people have called Haeckel's " frauds," which raised such a storm in Germany a few years before he died. His writings have been translated into many languages, and the uncritical public suppose that they represent the orthodox scientific thought along these lines. " Biologists to-day, however, are apt to look askance at Haeckel's works and to consider that they did more harm than good to Darwinism " (H. H. Newman, *Readings*, p. 30).

As an example of Haeckel's very " uncritical use of materials," spoken of here by Newman, may be given his invention of a *Gastraea* animal to correspond to the gastrula stage of the human embryo, also his invention of an animal which he termed the *Coelomaea*, which would correspond to the stage of the human embryo where the coelom or body cavity first appears. This feature of Haeckel's use of the facts of embryology will be spoken of more fully in Chapter VII.

XI

August Weismann (1834-1914) is one of the most influential biologists of modern times. He undertook to supplement Darwin's theory with one of his own which has been called the theory of " germinal-selection," which was an endeavour to picture a contest as going on among the carriers of heredity in the germ cell. It was an endeavour to support Darwin's main theory of natural selection at two of its weakest points. " But the supporting theory itself has the fundamental weakness of lacking a factual basis. It is purely hypothetical and cannot be put to an experimental test. Every time an objection to the theory was raised an auxiliary hypothesis was added to explain away the difficulty, till finally it fell to the ground through sheer top-heaviness, unable further to support its intricate structure of interrelated hypotheses." (H. H. Newman, *Readings in Evolution, Genetics and Eugenics,*" p. 31.)

However, the thing by which Weismann is now remembered is his doctrine of the continuity or apartness of the germ-plasm, sometimes called the " germ-plasm theory." Weismann showed that very early in the development of the embryo, sometimes from its first cellular divisions, certain cells are always set aside to act as the producers of the new germ cells at the maturity of the organism. Thus the germ cell is not the product of the body, or the *soma,* as it is called; but the body is the offshoot of the germ cells. Thus the body becomes merely the carrier and protector of the germ-plasm, the latter being essentially immortal, passing from one generation to the next. As Conklin whimsically expressed it, " The hen does not produce the egg, but the egg produces the hen and also other eggs."

To quote again from Professor Newman:

" The logical conclusion to which this line of reasoning

leads is that the changes in the soma, no matter how produced, are helpless to produce any effect upon the germ plasm, since germ cells come only from germ cells and not from soma cells. Consequently Weismann led the assault against Lamarckism and won the day so conclusively that even in these modern times few biologists have the temerity to express aloud any definite belief in the inheritance of acquired characters." (*Readings*, p. 32.)

Weismann in Germany, with E. Ray Lankester, and A. R. Wallace in England, may be regarded as the leaders of " pure Darwinism," by which is meant that they held to the idea that natural selection is the sole, or at least the chief factor in the evolutionary process. To-day this position is held by many biologists, though there are also many others who would agree with the statement of John Burroughs, that Darwin " has already been shorn of his selection theories as completely as Samson was shorn of his locks " (*Atlantic Monthly*, August, 1920, p. 237).

XII

It would not be profitable for us to enter upon a detailed study of the many conflicting ideas which have been put forward during the last few decades, in an effort to find some new factor with which to explain the evolution of organisms. Hugo de Vries, a Dutch botanist, has contributed the idea of " mutations," by which is meant that quite distinct variations may occur suddenly, these new characters being passed along in heredity to the next generation. These mutations are about what Darwin and the other students of heredity of a former time spoke of as " sports;" though Darwin himself did not place much dependence upon these " sports " as possible sources of new and permanent characters. The work of De Vries has been almost obscured by the great vogue of Mendelian investigations; and whether "mutations" be considered as really originating something new in some mysterious method of origin, or whether they be regarded as merely the results of long latent hereditary factors now cropping out or released in some unknown manner, it is now quite generally admitted that there is no other method of heredity except the Mendelian.

Sir Francis Galton, a cousin of Charles Darwin, originated a method of studying variation and heredity by statistics, this statistical method being known as biometry. Karl Pearson is one of the leading exponents of this method. Biometry had a considerable vogue before the rise of Mendelism; since which time it has much declined in importance. "On the whole the contributions of biometry to our understanding of the causes of evolution are rather disappointing. About the only clean-cut finding has been the discovery that some variations are continuous and others discontinuous" (Newman). As has been explained in a previous chapter, these continuous variations are not hereditary and can be plotted on a frequency curve; while the discontinuous variations or mutations are strictly hereditary and can only be plotted on frequency curves of more than one mode.

Among the modern biologists who are outstanding exponents of Mendelian methods, may be mentioned William Bateson, Thomas Hunt Morgan, of Columbia, with many others. Bateson has suggested the idea that development has taken place through the steady loss of retarding or inhibiting factors. This idea that evolution has taken place chiefly by loss and not by gain, has not been received very seriously by orthodox evolutionists. Morgan has been engaged in studying the hereditary characters displayed by the fruit-fly, *Drosophila*, and has produced over 200 distinct types, or mutant characters, of this fly. He and his assistants have been the chief ones concerned in the study of the chromosomes and their behaviour, and it is to these workers that we owe the modern conception that these chromosomes are the actual carriers of all the hereditary qualities. In this way we seem to have hit upon the actual mechanism of heredity; though it is perhaps too soon to affirm that all of the actual machinery of heredity has been discovered.

The present anomalous situation in biology regarding these problems of heredity is well stated by Vernon Kellogg in a recent article. He shows how both Darwinism and Lamarckism have both been discredited; and he points with fine scorn at the utter inadequacy of the Darwinian explanation of specific differences. " Indeed," he says, " most of the species differences—let alone the individual differences—among such animals as the insects and others represented by large numbers of species, are of a kind which require a very lively imagination to see differences of life- and death-determining value " (*The New Republic*, April 11, 1923).

After pointing out how " mutations " are equally inadequate and unsatisfactory as explanations of how evolution has come about, he goes on to say:

" This sounds discouraging for the evolutionists. But it really is discouraging only to the seekers after the *causes* of evolution."

Yes; I suppose so. Those who still maintain their faith in the grotesque methods of evolutionary geology, who are confident that plants and animals have been steadily appearing in a definitely ascertained order of succession during uncounted millions of years, will continue to believe in organic development somehow; and the little detail of the failure of biology to show how this wonderful fact came about will not bother them very much. But for those who have had their eyes opened regarding the pseudo-scientific methods of evolutionary geology in arranging the fossils in an alleged historical or chronological order, this utter failure of modern biology to find a rational explanation of the *how* of the process of organic development, must tend to strengthen the suspicion that the biological sciences have for many decades been working along false lines entirely.

In addition to this recognized failure of modern biology to confirm the doctrine of organic evolution, we have already seen in the previous chapter that the botanists almost as an entire class are complaining about the complete failure of geology to help out in supporting the theory, so far as the fossil plants are concerned, one leading botanist saying that phylogeny, or the attempt to trace out evolutionary pedigrees, " is no science, but a product of fantastic speculations " (J. P. Lotsy); while another says that he also has " become skeptical of late as to most phylogenetic reconstructions " (D. H. Scott).

But the case is even worse yet. For the new developments in geology itself have clearly shown that the serial arrangement of the fossils in an alleged historical order is merely a big blunder. Accordingly, there is little wonder that a widespread revolt is now taking place against the entire evolution doctrine. And there is little wonder that the leaders of this doctrine, the old guard, are getting much concerned regarding the scientific standing of their theory, and are trying to reassure the public that a belief in the doctrine of organic evolution is absolutely universal among all modern scientists of repute.

The latter statement will be recognized for what it really is, a colossal bluff.

XIII

Certain it is that the deniers of organic evolution, who are also the believers in the New Catastrophism in geology, are the ones who are taking the scientifically *safe* attitude. They are the ones who are now maintaining the magnificent tradition of a natural science which repudiates fantastic speculations and rests upon facts and facts alone. They are the ones who are now carrying on to maintain the spirit of non-dogmatic science. The evolutionary theory showed its true character of intolerant dogmatism under the leadership of such men as Buffon, Oken, Lamarck, and Haeckel; and the modern leaders of the doctrine are also living up to their old tradition, in the face of rapidly accumulating adverse facts. The latter are the real obscurantists, the reactionaries. The true progressives and the best friends of modern science are the ones who are trying to hold to facts alone; but they can not be blamed for recognizing that the new discoveries are tending so remarkably to confirm the Bible record about the early days of the world. It is the standpatters in science who are complaining about these new lines of discovery, that each of these new revelations of the secret ways of nature is merely leading them up a blind alley, into a *cul-de-sac*, to an *impasse*, and is not contributing in any way to the further development of the evolution theory.

BIBLIOGRAPHY

Chamberlin, T. C., *Seventy-five Years of American Geology;
Science,* February 8, 1924.

Davidson, Percy E., *The Recapitulation Theory;* 1914.

Geikie, Sir A., *The Founders of Geology;* 1901.

Le Conte, Jos., *Evolution and Religious Thought;* 1899.

Mitchell, P. C., *Evolution,* in *Encycl. Brit.;* Vol. X, pp. 22-37.

Newman, H. H., *Readings in Evolution, Genetics, and Eugenics;* 1922.

Osborn, H. F., *From the Greeks to Darwin;* 1908.

Scott, D. H., *Extinct Plants and Problems of Evolution;* 1924.

Zittel, K., *History of Geology and Paleontology;* 1901.

V

SPECIES AND THEIR ORIGIN

I

THOSE who have lived amid the strikingly peculiar vegetation of desert regions, such as the southwestern part of the United States, will appreciate the statement that this desert flora is decidedly different from the vegetation of the more humid parts of the world. It has an individual character all its own; and the animals also of these regions are almost as distinctly peculiar to these parts. The flora and the fauna of the desert regions of the globe, or even of the more arid regions, seem to belong almost to a world of their own. In view of these facts it is surely a most interesting and a most remarkable fact that the fossiliferous strata do not contain any of these desert forms. In other words, these desert organisms have somehow become what they are; but such plants and animals do not seem to have existed in the former age of the world's history before the geological deposits were made. As it has been expressed by D. T. Macdougal, Director of the Desert Laboratory for Botanical Research, at Tucson, Arizona: "No fossil remains of desert plants have yet been recovered. Some of the forms which have the aspect of xerophytes [desert plants] must have grown in moist regions by reason of their method of reproduction." (*Outlines of Geologic History*, p. 297.)

What do these facts mean? They must mean that the present flora (and fauna) of the desert are the greatly modified descendants of other kinds of life which existed in the long ago. In other words, it must be that these modern plants and animals now found living in the deserts in various parts of the world have been produced, " evolved " if the reader prefers this term, from other kinds of plants and animals which by all scientists are regarded as distinct species. It would seem that no other conclusion is possible. For we shall hardly be prepared to say that these animals and plants were especially created *de novo,* after the close of the great world catastrophe which the New Geology has revealed to us. The only other alternative would be to suppose that these kinds of life had been in existence in the ancient world but had not left any fossils in the stratified rocks. Personally I consider the latter of these two suppositions quite as unreasonable as the former. It follows from this that we must regard these modern kinds of plants and animals as having been derived by natural processes of change from somewhat related kinds which are nevertheless considered to be distinct species, perhaps even distinct genera. Whether this descent with modifications was accomplished by a process of development upward, or by a degeneration downward, will be considered later.

It will thus be seen that we are driven to a belief in the origin of quite distinct " species " by some sort of natural process within the period of time embraced by human history, for it is quite well established that the human race antedates the great world convulsion revealed to us by geology.

Geological research has also very clearly proved that in the olden times a warm, temperate, springlike climate prevailed over the entire globe. Not only is this true at one period of the past, but as A. R. Wallace has expressed it, throughout the whole period covered by the geological deposits, " we find one uniform climatic aspect of the fossils." This means that there is only one kind of climate known to geology proper.

But in view of this fact there must be a great many kinds of animals, and some plants, found in the Arctic and Antarctic regions of our modern world which must be quite as truly the modified descendants of other plants and animals which lived in that mild antediluvian climate of the long ago. True, such forms as the reindeer, the musk ox, and the glutton may be regarded as having been adapted to the high mountains or table-lands of that ancient world, which would naturally have had a climate somewhat cooler than the lands near the sea-level. But all the evidence would tend to show that these modern Arctic floras and faunas must be the greatly modified descendants of kinds of plants and animals which scientists would without doubt class as very distinct species. Thus we may say that the plants and animals of the polar latitudes teach us the same lesson as do the floras and faunas of the desert. Obviously, living organisms *have* undergone considerable change in passing from that ancient world to our modern one.

These are extremely well-attested facts; and it behooves us to consider how such changes could have been brought about. And if the investigations inspired by Darwinism and Mendelism can help us in any way to solve this problem, we ought to be willing to accept their help in this respect. Personally I feel that a residiuum of truth has been revealed by these biological studies in heredity and variation; because if it had not been for these studies we could not understand how such changes could possibly have been brought about.

II

The vexed question of what is a " species," is best understood by some historical facts.

Our binomial nomenclature comes to us from Linnaeus (1707-1778), who wished to include under a species all those organisms which owe their origin to some pair originally created. This was an understandable idea, but of little use in systematic classification. However, the idea of species as distinct groups of animals or plants which are much alike and also quite unlike others, has survived, in spite of the efforts of some scientists of a generation ago to make it appear that there is no such distinct and delimited group as a species. The efforts of the latter were quite consistent with Darwinism; but with the cloud now resting over the doctrines of both Darwin and Lamarck, the idea of species has been vindicated, and is to-day more firmly established than ever before.

Linnaeus made provision in his system for the effects of degeneration, and also for the results of hybridization. With this view of the matter, he was naturally opposed to a very minute set of characters as constituting the grounds for specific distinctions, he wished to look at plants and animals in a broad, common-sense fashion. For example, he included the primrose, the cowslip, and the true oxlip all under one species, making each of these mere varieties. His dictum was, *Varietates levissimas non curat botanicus,* the botanist ignores minute varieties.

But the French botanist, Jordan, undertook to test out the permanency of various kinds of plants by growing them; and he found that much more minute distinctions than those of Linnaeus *could* be recognized and would be found to *breed true to seed*. This was all before the days of Mendelism and modern genetics; but this idea of *physiological species,* as those of Jordan have been called, has been followed by most botanists and zoologists ever since, with the result that more and more minute specific distinctions have been made; species have been elevated into genera, and genera into families, while the pleasant task of species mongering has gone merrily on, to the confusion of all but the narrowest specialists, and the despair of those who wish to study the great problems of organisms in a broad philosophic way.

With the rise of Mendelism and the prevalence of experimental breeding, we now see that great multitudes of Jordanian species are only Mendelian segregates which somehow continue to maintain their separateness in nature. We are even beginning to suspect that some of the species of Linnaeus may also be of this character. In the field of botany, this more modern and more liberal view of the subject is well represented by the monumental work now being carried on by Harvey M. Hall and Frederic E. Clements, under the auspices of the Carnegie Institution of Washington. In zoology, I am not aware that anybody has attempted a similar line of work. While of course no glimmer of this new light has yet filtered down among the paleontologists, where the absurd methods long ago pointed out by Zittel (*History of Geology and Palæontology,* pp. 375, 400) are still the order of the day. Bateson once gave the systematists the ironic advice to list and describe all the " new " species which they could induce any reputable journal to print; but this becomes a dangerous kind of joke when the species-mongers occupy influential positions and can get their lists and descriptions published at Government expense. In the case of living plants and animals, experimental breeding may be employed to test out the soundness of some of these new specific names; but what is the remedy in the case of the fossil trilobites, or brachiopods, or ammonites, when the newer books try " to restrict the generic and specific distinctions within the narrowest possible limits, in order to enhance the value " (?) of these fossils " for the characterization of stratigraphical horizons " (Zittel, p. 400)?

Fifty years ago Jordan recognized 200 species of *Draba verna;* while the U. S. Department of Agriculture now recognizes 250 kinds of wheat, " all of which breed true," as Hall and Clements remind us, " and would thus come to be species." They also tell us that in North American botany, " the great majority of real species had been described by the close of Gray's work, and the vast increase of species since that time chiefly represents a change of personal views as to the criteria that mark this unit." For example, in the past thirty years, and within merely the Rocky Mountain region alone, the number of genera has increased from 551 to 950; while the number of species has mounted from 1,905 to 5,100 (*The Phylogenetic Method in Taxonomy,* pp. 10-15; 1923). These authors are trying to call a halt in this mad scramble to manufacture new names; and declare that " if taxonomy is to be either stable or usable, it must rest upon the species concept of Linnaeus and the practice of eminent taxonomists from his time to the present " (p. 15).

These studies carried on by Hall and Clements seem

to be of great value in helping us to understand how new types of plants,—new " species," if you will,—are being produced by nature. These authors emphasize the fact that " direct adaptation to the habitat has there produced the largest number of new forms of plastic species. Mutation now seems less important than it did fifteen years ago " (p. 23). They seem to consider that the number of probable hybrids produced naturally in the field is relatively very small. " In spite of the changing importance of the methods of origin, it still appears certain that adaptation, mutation, variation, and hybridization comprise the four processes of evolution, though it now seems evident that adaptation and hybridization constitute the two basic modes " (p. 23).

III

We may illustrate the results which have been accomplished along this line with a few specific examples. There are now in existence some 40 or 50 species of cats, of the family of the *Felidae,* scattered throughout almost all the regions of the globe. But there is no doubt in my mind that they have all sprung from a common ancestry. There are some seven species of the *Equidae,* or horses, and they likewise are probably all of one common ancestry. The fact that many of these modern species of horse are now not cross-fertile with one another, does not seem to me to be of any scientific significance, save, perhaps, that time and degenerative tendencies may be the cause of this barrier of infertility; or this may be regarded as merely one of the wise provisions of nature for developing and maintaining that wide variety of types which it seems the especial glory of nature to produce.

We may further illustrate these principles by the twenty-odd species of pigs (genus *Sus*), which are also cosmopolitan in range. Flower and Lydekker, leading English authorities on mammals, are of the opinion that all of these various races of wild pigs would probably " breed freely together." For a long time it was considered that the various species of brown bears of Europe and Asia, as well as the grizzly bear of North America, are probably only well-marked varieties; and recent investigations seem to make them all identical with the gigantic ancient bear (*Ursus spelaeus*) found in the fossil state in the Pleistocene deposits of the Old World; but there is no doubt in my mind that all of our modern species of bears must be of a common descent.

If these facts and these concessions on my part are of any comfort to the orthodox evolutionists, they are welcome to make the most of them. To my mind the followers of Darwin and of Mendel have been merely preparing the way for a truer and more rational view of the methods by which our present floras and faunas have been produced. In other words, they are merely the hewers of wood and the drawers of water for those of our day who are now gaining a more accurate insight into that marvelous record of the origin of our present plants and animals which is the very quintessence of modern scientific discovery, discoveries which so wonderfully confirm the record in the Christian's Bible.

IV

There has been a great deal of unthinking ridicule heaped upon the doctrine of " special creation," as it used to be termed. Charles Darwin, who was usually so polite and considerate of his opponents, always treated with the utmost scorn this idea of a special creation. Indeed, he seems never to have understood the real meaning of creation as a philosophical conception. As Mivart has said, " None but the crudest conceptions are placed by him to the credit of the supporters of the dogma of creation, and it is constantly asserted that they, to be consistent, must offer ' creative fiats ' as explanations of physical phenomena, and be guilty of numerous other such absurdities. . . . He has the appearance of opposing ideas which he gives no clear evidence of having ever fully appreciated. He is far from being alone in this, and perhaps merely takes up and reiterates, without much consideration, assertions previously assumed by others." (*The Genesis of Species*, pp. 28, 29.)

As the matter stood in Darwin's day, with the long succession of geological formations regarded as an actual historical fact, and with these successive groups of life appearing one after another in a true historical sequence, as it was then regarded, the " special creations " thus demanded would be a great many successive acts of creation, spread out at intervals over many millions of years; and there is not much wonder that Darwin and others regarded all this as quite unreasonable. But this was a mere burlesque of the true idea of a direct creation, as taught in the Bible. This burlesque of creation, this creation on the installment plan, had been handed down from the speculations of Buffon and Baron Cuvier; but our modern geological discoveries have put this whole idea completely out of consideration. For, as has been stated in a previous chapter, and as has been abundantly shown by the writings of the present author elsewhere, there is no possible way of proving in a strictly scientific manner that any of these sets of fossils really lived and died before others. Thus in our day we no longer have to deal with a long succession of creations, but with *one act of creation,* which may easily be supposed to have included all of those ancestral types from which our modern varieties of plants and animals have been derived.

V

If now we undertake to compare this modern phase of the doctrine of a direct creation with either of its rivals, the series of creations on the installment plan, as taught by Cuvier, or the development of the higher types from the lower, as taught by Darwin and his followers, the doctrine of creation is seen to have very many arguments in its favour.

In our day, and in the light of all that we now know regarding the laws of organisms, it is easier for us to believe in the doctrine of creation than in the theory of evolution. We are all familiar with the fact that life can come only from antecedent life; because of this we have to believe in the creation of the first living forms, or else hold to an unproved theory of the possibility of spontaneous generation. Thus the doctrine of creation is no more unreasonable than is the now universally accepted belief in biogenesis. For if we may suppose the Creator to have undertaken to start life at all, we may as well suppose that at this same general time He created full-grown specimens of the various distinct plants and animals with which He desired the world should be inhabited. For a Being who wished and who had the power to create the first speck of protoplasm (an act quite unknown to modern science, and thus a purely " supernatural " act) must have been capable of creating *any number of kinds* of distinct plants and animals. And the creation of this original stock of organic life is no more intrinsically improbable or unreasonable than is the creation of that first elementary form from which Darwinists suppose all other subsequent forms have been derived.

VI

There are other classes of species which have also clearly been produced in some manner by the modern processes of nature. Such I believe are the blind fishes and other animals found in such localities as the Mammoth Cave. When these blind fishes were first brought to the attention of scientists, Professor Agassiz, who was committed to the doctrine of the " fixity " of species and to the doctrine of a great many successive creations, took the absurd position that these blind fishes " were created under the circumstances in which they now live, within the limits over which they now reign, and with the structural peculiarities which now characterize them."

But since the days of the Prophet of Penikese other dark caverns have been examined in various parts of the world, and some very remarkable facts have been found.

1. Many other classes of animals besides fishes have been found in dark caves.

2. In all caves that are totally dark all of the animals are blind.

3. Where the animals live near enough to the entrance to receive some slight degree of light, they may have large and lustrous eyes.

4. In each case the blind animals found in a cave are closely related to species inhabiting the district where they occur; that is, the blind species inhabiting

caves in America are like the American species, while those found in European caves are closely similar to European species, and in Australia the cave animals resemble the Australian species.

5. In many instances the structural remnants of eyes have been detected, in various degrees of obsolescence. Some of the crustaceans of the Mammoth Cave have foot-stalks of eyes, although the eyes themselves are entirely absent. (H. H. Newman.)

In such instances as this, it seems to me quite evident that we are dealing with changes of structure and of habits of life which have clearly been brought about by what we usually term "adaptation," since the present configuration of land surface was established, that is, since the universal Deluge, to use the language of the New Catastrophism. Just as we have found in the case of the desert plants and animals, where the present species have undoubtedly arisen from somewhat related forms in adaptation to the arid surroundings, so here in these lightless, underground regions we have other types of life which have likewise become adapted to their present abnormal habitats.

I am not sure but that many of the so-called rudimentary structures, sometimes called vestigial structures, might very properly be explained in this way. The crustaceans of the Mammoth Cave which have merely the foot-stalks of eyes, are clearly instances of this sort. Whether the vestigial hind limbs of the python are to be explained in this way might be a matter of question. Possibly the rudimentary wings of the *Apteryx australis* and other flightless birds may be explained in the same manner. The many species of wingless beetles on ocean islands may be explained as having been produced by similar adaptations.

As to how these eyeless fishes or wingless insects or birds may have arisen, Thomas Hunt Morgan makes some remarks, based on his now famous experiments with the fruit fly. He has produced both eyeless and wingless varieties; but in all cases these mutants have not been produced by a gradual process, the result of the summation of many smaller variations, but by one bound.

"Formerly," says Morgan, "we were taught that eyeless animals arose in caves. This case shows that they may arise suddenly in glass milk bottles, by a change in a single factor.

"I may recall in this connection that wingless flies also arose in our cultures by a single mutation. We used to be told that wingless insects occurred on desert islands because those insects that had the best developed wings had been blown out to sea. Whether this is true or not, I will not pretend to say; but at any rate wingless insects may also arise, not through a slow process of elimination, but at a single step." (*A Critique of the Theory of Evolution,* p. 67.)

From all this it is evident that profound changes in plants and animals have occurred since the present order of things was established, or since the world catastrophe of the Deluge. But it is equally evident that these changes probably did not take place by Darwinian methods. More than likely the latter have had nothing at all to do with these changes. And instead of these changes of structure or of instinct requiring long ages for their accomplishment, they could have been completed very quickly.

VII

And it seems to me that these facts help us to understand some of the problems connected with the origin of the races of mankind.

The races of mankind greatly resemble true species. Indeed, in the days of Agassiz the human race was thought to be made up of several distinct species. The more prominent races, such as the negro, the Caucasian, and the Mongolian, do not differ from one another by merely one or two characters, but by many associated ones. Probably a dozen or more characters could be enumerated in respect to which the negro differs from the white man. True, these races prove to be cross-fertile; but so do great numbers of natural species among plants and animals. In many other respects also the races of mankind greatly resemble the best marked Linnaean species among animals and plants.

On the other hand, we have no historic record of how these races arose. *We are just as much in the dark regarding their origin as we are regarding the origin of the common species of plants and animals found wild in nature.* For, on the monuments of Egypt, recording the state of mankind at the very dawn of authentic history, the races of man are shown both by outline and by colour to have been quite as distinct as at the present day. Evolutionists have always argued that long unrecorded ages must have preceded these early Egyptian records. But in the light of the genetic facts revealed by Mendelism, why may we not suppose that the races of mankind arose suddenly, in accord with the sudden (or at least rapid) origin of many new forms in deserts, or caves, or other abnormal situations?

It is certain that very abnormal conditions must have prevailed immediately after the Deluge, not only for all the animals and plants, but also for man. The plentiful supply of vegetation had been swept away, and the earth was a vast wilderness. The climate, too, must have been very different from that which formerly prevailed. A warm, spring-like climate had formerly been universal over the earth; now terrific extremes of heat and cold were the rule. With nearly one fourth of the land surface even now forming *interior basins*, without outside drainage to the ocean, we must suppose that all of these basins were, immediately after the Deluge, full to the brim with water. And it would take centuries of evaporation to make any material change in these conditions. The entire body of the water of the ocean must have been warm before the Deluge; but immediately thereafter a rapid cooling of this water set in, which, however, would still leave all the warm water on the surface, perhaps for centuries. Both of these causes must have combined to render the climate of all the northern lands very cold and damp for many centuries. Fogs and bleak weather must have been well-nigh continuous; the precipitation must have been enormous; and the accumulating masses of snow and ice must have pushed rapidly down from the mountain ranges in the form of prodigious glaciers. In this modified sense of the term, the " glacial age " is not a myth but a reality. But it is evident that mankind and all his companion animals must have found themselves amid an environment very radically different from anything which they had been accustomed to before.

And we may be very sure that the great superintending Power which is over nature, adapted these men and these animals and plants to their strange world. That healing power which quickly covers over a wounded branch, or which rapidly restores a bleeding back or a broken leg, could be depended upon without question to set about the rapid transformation of that seemingly ruined world into one which, while not at all equal to the marvelous one before the Flood, is yet a very beautiful and well-ordered habitation for man and his companion animals.

The believer in the Bible will also point out a moral and social reason for the differentiation of mankind into distinct races. He reads in the early record of the post-diluvian world that all of mankind were of one speech and of one race; but that design-ing men started to make capital out of this fact, and attempted to consolidate all under one rule and one system of worship, which evidently was an apostate system. The record is that God again interfered, and broke up the scheme, scattering the fragments of the race abroad upon the face of the earth. And just as artificial barriers of language were interposed to keep them from again blending into one world-embracing despotism, so we may well suppose that the barriers of race and colour were also interposed at this same time, these racial barriers assisting in segregating the people of the world off into self-contained groups, thus most effectually preventing them from ever again unit-ing. And there is no doubt that if human beings had always been as true to natural instincts as are the spe-cies among the higher animals, there never would have been amalgamation among these races which had thus been set apart from one another by a special interven-tion of Providence.

This, it seems to me, is the best and most reasonable explanation of the origin of the races of mankind. It is supported by the facts of archaeology, which show us these races at the very dawn of history apparently just as distinctly marked as at present. It is also supported by the facts of philology; for we learn that there are probably fifty or more distinct groups of languages, so completely distinct that we cannot imagine how they could possibly have had a common origin. In both respects the Bible record of the Dispersal of mankind soon after the Deluge furnishes by far the most believable explanation of the facts as we now know them through archaeology and philology.

VIII

It will not be necessary for us to pause here to consider the hard circumstances amid which these world-pioneers began to build up homes and civilizations in favoured localities, like the Valley of the Nile, or around the basin of the Mediterranean, or along the Euphrates. Rather must we consider briefly the character of the changes which have been produced in man and the animals by their transplantation from the world before the Deluge into the world as we now know it. Has the general trend of these changes been upward or downward? How do the modern forms compare with those of the antediluvian world? Has there been development or degeneration?

There can be but one answer, by any one acquainted with those superb, those giant forms among the larger mammals which were man's brute companions before the world disaster, and which are still found living in various parts of the modern world. Whether we consider the huge Pleistocene elephants, or the lion, the bear, the hippopotamus, the rhinoceros, or the elk, found as fossils in these deposits, or whether we descend the scale of life and study the fishes, the insects, the crustaceans, the mollusks, the brachiopods, the birds, or the reptiles, we are constantly met with evidences that the fossil forms are larger and better shaped than their corresponding living representatives, if any allied families or genera are still alive in our modern world.[1] It is a uniform testimony of degeneration.

Sir William Dawson, in speaking on this point, and saying that degeneracy is the rule rather than the exception, whenever we compare the fossils with the modern forms, goes on to declare:

" We may almost say that all things left to themselves tend to degenerate, and only a new breathing of the Almighty Spirit can start them again on the path of advancement." (*Modern Ideas of Evolution, Appendix.*)

We have thus arrived at a philosophy of change among the species of plants and animals; and we find that there has indeed been an origin of " species " since the beginning of things. But contrary to the views of Darwin and his followers, the general results of these changes have not been of the nature of advancement. Degeneration seems to have dogged the steps of every created form; the few exceptions to this rule having been produced by the efforts of man.

But it is also worthy of remark that the change from the larger ancient forms to the smaller and more degenerate modern forms, seems to have come about

[1] NOTE.—All of the Pleistocene mammals were larger than their living representatives. *"Elephas antiquas,* for instance, attained a more excessive bulk than any other proboscidian either before or since, the woolly rhinoceros, the great hippopotamus, the cave bear, cave lion, and giant deer were all larger than their living representatives." (J. A. Howe, *Encycl. Brit.,* Vol. XXI, p. 836.) This fact of the larger size of the ancient forms, as compared with their living representatives (if they have any), is a universal characteristic of the fossils from the Cambrian to the Pleistocene.

abruptly in point of time, and to have been of world-wide extent, the change coinciding exactly with the world-wide changes recorded in the rocks, by which the ancient world was changed into the modern one.

We see the same general tendency toward degeneration when we consider man himself. Not, of course, if we let the evolutionists arrange the various skulls and skeletons according to their own ideas, beginning with *Pithecanthropus* and following along down past the Heidelberg jaw, the Piltdown skull, the Neanderthal skull, and the Cro-Magnards. As I have shown elsewhere, there is no reason whatever for arranging these specimens in this order (supposed to be historical) except to make this order illustrate the preconceived theory of man's animal origin. The reasons are based on the fossils and are wholly morphological; and as it is assumed that the lowest and most ape-like must have been first, these specimens from widely scattered localities are arranged to illustrate this idea. Does this arrangement *prove* anything? Well, nothing so clearly as the hypnotizing power of a preconceived theory.

Is there really anything to indicate that the Neanderthal man lived before those found at Cro-Magnon? Nothing whatever. Accordingly, while I do not admit that the latter are positively antediluvian, it is certain that they are very early postdiluvian; and in the absence of real specimens of antediluvian man, we may as well consider these Cro-Magnards, and note how they illustrate the same general tendency to large size and splendid physical development which we noted on the part of the Pleistocene mammals.

What sort of people were these which were found at Cro-Magnon, a cave near Dordogne, France?

The old man of Cro-Magnon was over six feet tall, with a skull which one authority says was equal to that of Bismarck; while Dawson says that the skeleton gives evidence " of immense muscular development." This man was evidently very old; for, though every tooth was sound, they were very greatly worn down. Sir A. Keith declares that this race " was the finest the world has ever seen," while Macnamara says, on the evidence from these skeletons, that the tradition about there having been a race of giants in the long ago " was no myth."   Several of these Cro-Magnon men were six feet four inches high.   Judged by the bones and skulls alone, which are absolutely the only criteria we have, unless we bring in also the wonderful paintings found in other localities of southern France, we must conclude that these Cro-Magnon people were away above the average men of to-day in both physical vigour and native mental capacity.   Indeed, Henry Fairfield Osborn has recently declared: " I have every reason to believe that the Cro-Magnon ' cave-man ' could enter any branch of the intellectual life of this university [Columbia] on equal, if not on superior terms with any of the 30,000 students here."

As already remarked, these men were probably not antediluvian, but only very early postdiluvian.   But they do resemble the antediluvian mammals in their large size and splendid development.   And we can judge from them that the real antediluvian human beings must have corresponded in size and structure with those giants of the prime which adorn so many of our great museums.   Such specimens as those from Heidelberg, Neanderthal, and Piltdown may be regarded as degenerate offshoots which had separated from the main stock both ethnically and geographically. It is one of the burning shames of modern scientific investigations that grotesque speculations have long occupied the world under such headings as professedly scientific accounts of the *Men of the Old Stone Age,* and various other publications professing to deal with the subject of the antiquity of man. The vagaries of astrology, of phrenology, or of spiritualism, present no more absurdly unscientific methods than those which have so long prevailed in the name of archæological science. For there is no sufficient proof that these notorious specimens just mentioned are really very old; there is no possible way of proving their *relative* antiquity; and furthermore there is no evidence that these few stray specimens represent anything but abnormal freaks which may have been quite different from the majority of the types of mankind then prevailing.

Thus in all these various respects we have a plain record of the general direction in which variation and change has progressed since those remote days when the geological animals left their remains in the strata of Europe and America. And it seems to me that these patent proofs of a general tendency to degenerate ought always to be borne in mind whenever we consider the changes which have certainly taken place in producing our present faunas and floras of such regions as our deserts and our Arctic regions, which certainly were not in existence before the Deluge. If such facts as these had always been kept in mind when studying these matters, there would have been less confusion in the conclusions based on these peculiarly modern conditions. We should see that, while the providence of the Creator has wisely adapted species to these strange and hitherto unknown conditions, the general results of these changes has not been in the direction of larger form or better structural development.

BIBLIOGRAPHY

Bateson, Wm., *Mendel's Principles of Heredity;* 1909.
　　　　　　　　Evolutionary Faith and Modern Doubts; Science, January 20, 1922.

Conklin, E. G., *Heredity and Environment;* 1921.

Fairhurst, Alfred, *Organic Evolution Considered;* 1913.

Hall (H. M.) and Clements (F. E.), *The Phylogenetic Method in Taxonomy;* 1923.

Lock, Robert Heath, *Variation, Heredity and Evolution;* 1920.

Morgan, Thos. H., *A Critique of the Theory of Evolution;* 1916.
　　　　　　　　The Physical Basis of Heredity; 1919.
　　　　　　　　The Mechanism of Mendelian Heredity (joint author); Revised Edition, 1922.

Scott, D. H., *The Present Position of the Theory of Descent; Nature,* September 29, 1921.

Thomson, J. A., *Heredity;* 1919.

Zittel, K., *History of Geology and Paleontology;* 1901.

VI

TOO MANY ANCESTORS

I

PROFESSOR E. W. MacBride, the eminent embryologist of England, has given us some very illuminating remarks regarding the embryology and the classification of the various invertebrates. In speaking of the classification of the starfishes, he alludes to the common custom of shaping up the classification largely on the theoretical assumption of just how the various orders have developed from simpler beginnings. This method of attempting to determine the number of orders in this group has been the cause of much dispute among the scientists interested in the study of these animals. And he goes on to remark that:

"The attempt to construct detailed phylogenies involves the assumption that one set of structures, which we take as the mark of the class, has remained constant, whilst others which are regarded as adaptive, may have been developed twice or thrice. As the two sets of structures are often of about equal importance, it will be seen to what an enormous extent the personal equation enters in the determination of these questions." (*Cambridge Natural History*, Vol. I, p. 460.)

These words bring out one of the very serious difficulties in connection with the evolution theory. They mean that in the attempt to trace the line of descent for any of the higher types of animal, such as man, it becomes quite impossible to obtain united agreement among evolutionists as to the exact course of this development, the route along which the higher forms have traveled. For instance, Darwin thought that man is descended from some of the arboreal apes which formerly existed. It is now more commonly asserted that he is descended from a type of ape which never lived in the trees. Also, in tracing his descent backwards into the far distant past, Darwin had man passing through the bird stage, while most modern evolutionists leave out this bird stage entirely, and bring man up directly from the reptiles. Indeed, if we trace out in detail any single organ of any of the leading types of animals, we always find ourselves confronted with this same difficulty. We have to decide (quite arbitrarily) that we will follow chiefly one set of structures, to the exclusion of others; that is, we have to assume that some one particular structure is the infallible hall-mark of the line of descent which we are tracing, and we have to assume that this one structure or set of structures has remained constant for long ages, while other structures which we think are not significant have been left behind or discarded. But presently we find that some very characteristic structures or organs must, on this basis, have been developed independently many times over, if we take the animals of the world as a whole; that is, they must have been *repeatedly developed independently*. And, as MacBride says, as the two sets of structures, the ones we are following and the ones we choose to disregard, " are often of about equal importance, it will be seen to what an enormous extent the personal equation enters in the determination of these questions."

The purpose of the present chapter is a comparative

study of the organs of various animals, and to consider whether the evolutionary explanation of these structures does not involve too many absurdities to make it possible for us longer to tolerate such an explanation of their origin.

II

Preliminary to this study, we need to understand two terms, *homology* and *analogy,* as used in biology. The fore limbs of man, of a dog, and of a bird, are said to be *homologous,* because they are said to originate in the embryo from identical structures and to develop similarly, although in maturity they are used for widely different purposes, that is, they have different functions. But the wing of an insect, the wing of a bird, the wing of a bat, and the wing of a pterodactyl, a kind of flying reptile, are said to be *analogous,* but not *homologous;* because, though used in maturity for the same purpose, they have had a different origin and are even now different in structure.

Such studies as these, in comparing the structures of various organisms, are embraced under the general term *morphology,* or the science of organic forms. And as Dr. Arthur Willey says, " Morphology, in the modern sense, usually conveys a genetic meaning, implying *morphogeny,* or the origin of forms " (*Convergence in Evolution,* p. 1). This author goes on to say that morphology " is the child of evolution, reared under the tutelage of Cuvier and Lamarck, Von Baer and Haeckel, Darwin and Huxley, and taken into the service of comparative anatomy and embryology " (*Ib., id.*).

Thus we are confronted with distinct evolutionary meanings which have been injected into the very terms and ideas which we are compelled to use in our discussion. And we are led to ask, How far has the "personal equation" also entered into the use and the accepted meaning of these terms? We find that we must at least be on our guard, if we wish to do clear and independent thinking.

If we say that the wings of a bird, of a bat, of an insect, and of a pterodactyl are *analogous,* but not *homologous,* we mean by these terms that we suppose that these four organs of flight have not been evolved from one another in any instance, but that each set has been evolved independently. And all this is in spite of the fact that the wing of the pterodactyl was a large, fully developed membranous wing, almost exactly like that of a bat; and that the former animal was doubtless as expert a flyer as the latter, which we know can fly with all the ease of a bird. No one claims that the wing of the bat has developed from the wing of the bird, although in all four instances mentioned there is a very similar adaptation of the fore limbs for use as organs of flight. Evolutionists have to admit that all four kinds of wings have been developed independently and as it were *de novo.* In other words, in trying to trace the evolution of the bat from its alleged reptilian ancestors, we have to say that the limbs have *not* remained constant, but that *other* structures have done so; and we have to assume that wings in the instances just mentioned have developed at least three times, perhaps four times, quite independently of each other.

III

Henry Fairfield Osborn has told us that it is very essential for us to distinguish between true hereditary

resemblances and those multiple forms of adaptive resemblance which are often spoken of by evolutionists
as examples of parallelism or parallel development.
" This wide distinction," he says, " between similarity
of descent and similarity of adaptation applies to every
organ, to all groups of organs, to animals as a whole,
and to all groups of animals " (*Encycl. Brit.*, Vol. XX,
p. 587). He goes on to say that analogy, or a superficial similarity, " in its power of transforming unlike
and unrelated animals or unlike and unrelated parts
of animals *into likenesses,* has done such miracles that
the inference of kinship is often almost irresistible.
During the past century it was and even now is the
very ' will-o'-the-wisp ' of evolution, always tending to
lead the phylogenist astray." This only means that
Professor Osborn has arbitrarily assumed that one set
of structures, which he takes as the sure mark of a
certain line of descent, has remained constant, while
he regards others as merely adaptive, the latter having
on this supposition developed independently two or
more times. And as these two sets of structures may
in reality, for ought that we know, be of about equal
importance, " it will be seen to what an enormous extent the personal equation " enters into the theory of
Osborn and his fellow-evolutionists, in their attempt
to trace the evolution of the various animal forms.

Dr. Osborn goes on to say that the shark, the ich-
thyosaur (a kind of fish-like reptile), and the dolphin,
a true, warm-blooded mammal, resemble each other
very strikingly in their general appearance. They all
look like fishes, whereas only one is a true fish, another
was a true reptile, and the third is a true mammal;
and it is impossible to suppose that the mammal has
developed directly from this reptile, or the reptile from

the fish, although they all look so very much alike. In this case, the internal structures of these animals are very different; but remarkable internal or skeletal transformations have also been produced, according to the evolutionists. "But the ingenuity of nature, in producing such adaptive transformations, is not infinite," says Osborn, "because the same devices are repeatedly employed by her to accomplish the same adaptive ends, whether in fishes, reptiles, birds, or mammals; thus she has repeated herself at least twenty-four times in the evolution of long-snouted rapacious swimming types of animals" (*Ib., id.,* p. 587).

We may conclude that "the personal equation" has entered very largely into the elaboration of such a scheme of evolution.

IV

A good example of the warping influence of this "personal equation," or the harmful effect of a theoretical bias, is shown by some remarks of George John Romanes in his discussion of comparative anatomy in his "Darwin and after Darwin." In comparing the fins of fishes with the legs of mammals, or the paddle of a whale with the hand of man, or the wing of a bird with the fore limb of a bat and of the pterodactyl, Romanes holds up to scorn the idea that the Deity has endeavoured to show His ingenuity by making the same kind of structure subserve many different functions. And he says that throughout the whole vegetable and animal kingdoms, "All cases which can be pointed to as showing ingenious adaptation of some typical structure to the performance of widely different functions— or cases of homology without analogy—are cases which come within the limits of the same natural group of plants and animals, and therefore admit of being equally well explained by descent from a common ancestor; while all cases of widely divergent structures performing the same function—or cases of analogy without homology,—are to be found in different groups of plants or animals, and are therefore suggestive of independent variations arising in the different lines of hereditary descent."

We have here an example of illogical or vicious reasoning which is very common to discussions of this class. Who is to say that the cases of homology without analogy always come within the *same natural group* of plants and animals? And why are they called the same " natural " group, except because of certain structures in which they are thought to be alike? *What is a natural group, anyway?* And *why* is it a natural group? Why is it that biologists cannot agree as to what is a natural group?

For instance, Dr. Franz Baron Nopsca has recently published a work on reptiles (*Die Familien der Reptilien,* Berlin, 1923). In this he gives us a new classification of the reptiles, and enumerates twelve other classifications which have been offered since 1890, his being the thirteenth. A reviewer in a recent number of *Science,* says that the radical differences of opinion in these classifications is " largely due to the fact that each author has considered a different character or group of characters as of importance." This reviewer congratulates himself on the fact that classifications in biology are to-day based "entirely upon genetic relationships," a fact which some of us think may be as much of an evil as a good. The only point I am expressing here is that this mania for basing modern classifications entirely on alleged " genetic relationships," does not tend to reassure our minds when we come to consider calmly such a question as we have propounded above, namely, " What is a *natural group* of plants and animals?" " Why is one grouping any more ' natural ' than another?"

The reviewer of Dr. Nopsca's recent book laments the fact that the materials at the disposal of the paleontologists are still far too limited " to permit a selection of the characters which reveal most accurately this genetic relationship; the personal factor is still prominent in each suggested classification. The most crying need in systematic paleontology to-day is a determination of what structures are fundamental in the development of any phylum and the direction of their evolutionary changes, as opposed to the secondary adaptive changes." (*Science,* December 21, 1923, p. 517.)

In the light of this discussion, if we now consider the argument of Romanes, we see how arbitrary it was for him to assume that certain groupings of animals are " natural " and that other groupings are not natural. In other words, Romanes in the quotation given above is merely reasoning in a circle, merely begging the question. Theologians and philosophers have often been caught at such tricks of logic, but our leading scientists have usually been thought free from such rhetorical devices. Of course, it might be very unfair to accuse Romanes of being consciously deceptive in this line of argument. It would be more urbane, at least, on my part, to assume that he was intellectually honest, but that he had not eliminated the personal factor and did not see the vicious nature of his line of reasoning. However this may be, it is certain that

Professor Romanes, in the quotation given above, has not made any substantial contribution to this discussion. In his case, as in that of other evolutionists, this whole line of argument from morphology is vitiated by the fact that *certain structures are always arbitrarily assumed to remain constant, while certain other structures are assumed to change with the utmost ease and frequency;* and accordingly when two identical structures are found in widely " separated " or " unrelated " groups which nevertheless perform a similar function, they are treated by biologists as " false homologies." But other structures which are similarly situated but which perform different functions, are arbitrarily regarded as being analogous but not homologous, though having originated by adaptation through a long series of successive evolutions.

V

It is to the intricacies of these questions that the attention of the reader is invited in this chapter. We shall see that, according to the evolution theory, very many structures must have arisen repeatedly and quite independently of each other. Thus it would appear that any particular type of animal, such as man, an elephant, or a turtle, may have had its most essential characters often duplicated by other animals which are not at all related to it by descent. Or, if we should follow out all of the lines of descent suggested by all of the various structures of any particular animal, we should find that this animal has had far too many possible ancestors; he literally has ancestors among the mollusks, or among the reptiles, or among the fishes; and this multiplication of possible lines of genetic descent seems to me one of the most serious objections to the whole scheme of organic evolution as commonly understood. At least, as it seems to me, these facts completely and conclusively demolish the argument which has so long been based upon morphology or comparative anatomy. I do not believe that the reader who will calmly consider the evidence now available will regard this argument from morphology as of any possible scientific value. It would be just as sensible to assume that a wheelbarrow developed into a bicycle, that the bicycle evolved into a tricycle, the latter becoming transformed into a buggy, and again into an automobile, and lastly into a sixteen-wheeled locomotive, as to believe that the structures of comparative anatomy prove anything at all regarding the genetic history of the higher animals.

VI

In further elaboration of this idea, that certain structures are arbitrarily assumed to have remained constant, while other structures are assumed to have varied or to have originated independently two or more times, we have the following also from H. F. Osborn:

" From comparative anatomy alone it is possible to arrange a series of living forms which, although structurally a convincing array because placed in a graded series, may be, nevertheless, in an order inverse to that of the actual historical succession. The most marked case of such inversion in comparative anatomy is that of Carl Gegenbauer (1826-1903), who in arranging the fins of fishes in support of his theory that the fin of the Australian lung-fish (Ceratodus) was the most primitive (or archipterygium), placed as the primordial type a fin which paleontology has proved to be one of the latest types if not the last." (*Encycl. Brit.*, Vol. XX, p. 586.)

But I wonder why Dr. Osborn never thought of these facts and principles when he permitted his colleagues to arrange the various fossil " horses " and other animals which are on exhibit to illustrate evolution in the great Museum in New York City of which he is the President. Here we have several series of skeletons and parts of skeletons, each of which, " although structurally a convincing array because placed in a graded series," may not in reality represent an historical order at all, and hence may be nothing better than child's play, so far as illustrating evolution is concerned. In the light of the newer discoveries in geology, who is to guarantee that the series of fossil horses, or camels, or elephants, as shown in that Museum, represent true historical sequences, or any historical sequence at all, for that matter? Because all of these fossil horses may have lived contemporaneously; and the same is true also of the elephants and the camels. When placed in the " graded series," as there shown, they may from comparative anatomy alone appear to be structurally a very " convincing array " for the deceiving of school children, who visit this Museum at the rate of nearly a million annually; but who that thinks clearly can be otherwise than amused at such unscientific methods of " proving " a pet theory?

VII

In the early days of this controversy, St. George Mivart, the accomplished biologist of London, devoted a chapter of his *Genesis of Species,* to " the co-existence of closely similar structures of diverse origin." This chapter covers over thirty pages, and in it Professor Mivart gives many striking examples of similar structures which must have had an entirely independent origin. He does not think that these examples tell against the general theory of evolution, providing we may suppose the latter process to have been superintended and directed by a creative Intelligence; but he argues that it is quite improbable and practically impossible " for two exactly similar structures to have ever been independently developed " by the action of natural selection alone. But it seems to me that these facts do make quite improbable and incredible the entire theory of organic evolution. I will concede that a directing Intelligence *could* have produced all the great variety of organic forms by such a process of organic development; but I utterly refuse to consider this as a probable explanation of their origin. It demands too much credulity on our part to believe such a theory. It is far easier to believe in the direct creation of all the leading types (e. g., the families), as explained elsewhere, though allowing for many minor variations under each of these larger groups.

One of the striking examples given by Mivart is the thylacine, or so-called Tasmanian wolf, which is so strikingly like a wolf or a dog in general appearance that at a distance the two cannot be distinguished. The thylacine is confined to the island of Tasmania; but it is a *marsupial* and not a placental mammal at all. How did nature come to make such a parody of the wolf, if we suppose that both of these animals have been independently evolved from some remote common ancestral type?

Among the marsupials, or pouched animals, there are carnivorous, insectivorous and herbivorous types which correspond not only in habits but also in many structural features to the similar carnivorous, insectivorous, and herbivorous mammals. Professor Huxley about 1866 proposed the theory that the placental mammals of these various groups must have been evolved directly from the corresponding marsupials. However, this theory has not been accepted by other evolutionists.

There are many points of similarity between the reptiles and the birds; the pterodactyls or flying reptiles, as already pointed out, have certain structures resembling those of carinate or flying birds; while the dinosaurs were structurally somewhat similar to the struthious or flightless birds. And Mivart declares, " either birds must have had two distinct origins whence they grew to their present uniformity, or the very same skeletal, and probably cerebral characters, must have spontaneously and independently arisen " (*The Genesis of Species,* p. 85).

Professor Mivart goes on to show that the cuttle-fishes, a group of mollusks, have elaborately constructed ears which serve the creatures as auditory organs, and which closely resemble in structure the similar organs found in the higher land animals. But as no one could possibly imagine that the higher vertebrates were derived by descent from these cuttle-fishes, we are driven to the conclusion that these highly complex organs of hearing must have been developed " in entire and complete independence of each other."

Charles Darwin is reported to have declared that the thought of the origin of the eye always gave him a cold shiver whenever he thought of the length of time involved in the production of such an organ. Now there are several distinct types of eyes in the animal kingdom. The eye of an insect is certainly a very efficient organ of sight; though it is constructed on a plan radically different from that of the vertebrates. But what is our surprise on finding in the cuttle-fishes an eye which is constructed on precisely the same general plan as that found in the vertebrates. In the eye of the cuttle-fish we find a true retina, a sclerotic, a choroid, a vitreous humour, an aqueous humour, and an adjustable lens, just as we find in the eye of one of the higher vertebrates. As Mivart says, " the correspondence is wonderfully complete; " and he argues that for such an exact, elaborate, and highly complicated series of similar structures to have been brought about in two independent instances by the hit-and-miss methods of minute chance variations, " is an improbability which amounts practically to impossibility." And I quite agree with him. Only I would go further and say that it seems absurd to suppose that two such parallel developments could ever have gone on without supposing more of the miraculous in the process of organic evolution than most of the advocates of this theory are inclined to admit.

If we were to enumerate the many instances where eyes are found which must have been developed quite independently, the list would be a long one. We may mention but one more, that of the pecten, a bivalve mollusk. This creature has a row of large and prominent eyes situated along the two edges of the mantle. Each of these eyes has an optic nerve, a cornea, a lens, and a choroidea, making it strikingly resemble the eye of a vertebrate. But it is evident that, if the evolution theory be true, this little mollusk must have evolved these wonderful structures quite independently of any similar structure in any other animal, even independent of the eye of the cuttle-fish.

The placental method of reproduction, by which the blood of the developing foetus is placed in intimate and nutritive relation with the blood of the mother, is another very remarkable structure which is found in certain sharks, as well as in the true mammals. No trace of such a structure exists in any reptile or bird; and it is preposterous to think that the mammals have descended (or ascended) from the sharks. Thus this highly complicated structure must have arisen quite independently in these two instances; and one is at a loss to understand how any such structure could possibly have developed by any process of slow, imperceptible variations, in accord with the evolution theory. But strange to say this very same structure is found also in certain ascidians, often called tunicates or sea-squirts. Now it will not help matters to suppose that these ascidians were the common ancestors of both the sharks and the higher mammals, for in the sharks the placenta is developed from the umbilical vesicle, while in the mammals it is developed from the allantois, a very different foetal structure. Moreover, it is quite out of the question for evolutionists to put the sharks in the direct line between the ascidians and the mammals. Accordingly, we are driven to the conclusion that the placental method of reproduction must have been developed in all three of these instances quite independently.

Mr. Mivart goes on to enumerate many other examples of this kind, for such parallelisms of structure appear throughout the whole of the animal kingdom. It would take an entire volume to enumerate all of such instances. Mivart only argues that the chance variations of Darwin are quite insufficient to account for such parallel structures. To my notion the argument is even stronger yet. It seems to me that these parallel structures in widely separated forms of life show that the whole theory of organic evolution, as commonly understood, is working along a wrong line entirely.

Our studies of both plants and animals have impressed us very strongly with the facts of heredity. We see a certain shape and colour in a cow, and we see the same shape and colour appear in her offspring. We have certain points in a dog which we wish to accentuate, and we carefully select its mate and have full confidence that we can produce by breeding the type which we desire. Here we see certain structures follow according to invariable law a line of heredity which we can demonstrate. And we are prone to think that similar structures in two distantly classified animals must somehow represent a common inheritance from some remote ancestor. But the facts which we have presented in the previous pages show that this is not always a true method of reasoning. If we follow out this rule, we shall get into serious trouble. We shall find that practically every single genus among the animal kingdom would, on this basis, seem to have far too many ancestors. A method of comparison which would lead us to say that the mammals were derived from the sharks or the sea-squirts, because of the placental structures common to all three, would also drive us to the conclusion that the modern mammals are descended from the cephalopod cuttle-fishes, because of the eyes and ears common to these two remote groups.

VIII

Thus, as our method of reasoning has led us into a palpable absurdity, we must retrace our steps and see where we are.

The lesson from all this is that we have in the animal kingdom a vast web of life, constructed on an elaborate plan of complicated similarities and dissimilarities, with such a profusion of individual types that it would seem to be impossible not to have many instances of similar or even identical structures in forms which are nevertheless widely removed from each other when considered on any rational basis of classification.

But if we wish to think clearly, we must constantly bear in mind the fact that our zoological and botanical classifications are very largely artificial, and within modern times have been rearranged repeatedly with the avowed purpose of making these classifications conform more closely with evolutionary theory. The classification of species into genera, and of genera into families, may be admitted to be quite natural and not artificial; though as we ascend to the *families* we find less agreement among systematists. When, however, we rise above the families, the classification of both plants and animals becomes more and more a matter of recording and illustrating evolutionary theories of supposed origins. That is, taxonomy becomes merely the servant of evolutionary phylogeny; and accordingly we must always be on the lookout for the evolutionary bias which surely lies embalmed in every system of classifying the families, orders, classes and phyla.

We may conclude that " descent with modification " will explain the origin of most of our species and genera, as descendants of some primal representatives of the *families;* but when we undertake to explain in this way the relationships between the *orders* and *classes* and *phyla,* we get into a field of sheer speculation, where a man has to shut his eyes to reason and common sense and go it blind.

In the days of Charles Darwin, it was supposed that geology had demonstrated that certain types of life actually lived and died long ages before others, and that the relative order in which the great types of life had come into existence on the globe had been established by proved facts. But we now know that this is all a blunder, and that the reptiles and amphibians cannot be proved to have lived long ages before the mammals, nor can it be proved that the various marsupials and " generalized " mammals actually lived before the higher mammals. Our misplaced confidence in the theories of the geologists and paleontologists, has made it seem that we had a long but well-defined outline of successive animals and plants, on which we have for nearly a century been trying to construct a detailed scheme of organic evolution. But with the collapse of the logic on which this geological series rests, we begin to see that a thoroughgoing scheme of organic evolution could never be made to work, even if this series of the fossils had been an actual historical series, instead of the purely artificial series which we know it really is.

We have learned many things about environment and heredity. We have learned quite a little about how plants and animals vary, and can imagine that at some time in the long ago " species " may have been even more plastic than at present. This will account for much of the great complexity which we see around us in our modern world. But to go beyond this, and to attempt to say that all our animals and plants have arisen from one original stock, or from two or three original stocks, taxes our credulity more than do the tales of Alice in Wonderland or those of the Arabian Nights. A belief in a real creation of a vast number of ancestral types from which the modern forms have descended by methods more or less known to us through the laws of heredity and variation, is far more reasonable than is the theory of organic evolution.

It would be tiresome to go through merely the many remarkable ways in which the marsupials resemble the mammals, though if evolution be true each of these similar kinds must have been produced independently among the two groups. Dr. Arthur Willey gives a diagram showing the parallel types, six in number, which are alike in the two classes, (1) the carnivorous, (2) the ant-eating, (3) the flying, (4) the swimming, (5) the large-eyed burrowing forms, and (6) the small-eyed burrowing forms. And he says that a similar diagram could be constructed to show the parallel series among the Insectivora and the Rodentia. It seems preposterous to tell us that in all these scores or hundreds of instances of striking outward resemblance, or of resemblance in habits and in internal structure, we are merely witnessing examples of parallel but quite independent evolution.

I do not believe a word of it. If these hundreds of mimics of one another have been produced by independent evolution, one is obliged to think that evolution can be invoked to account for anything. Perhaps, however, it would be more accurate to say that these many similar structures where genetic relationship is out of the question, tend to show that *homology is worthless as a proof of genetic relationship*.

IX

Let us take some other examples. A distinguished French zoologist of the last century declared that the ascidians (*Tunicata*) must be related to the mollusks.

In confirmation of this theory he discovered a species of *Molgula,* a simple ascidian, which undergoes direct development without the intervention of a tailed larva, such as most ascidians have. Presently he discovered another ascidian in the Mediterranean (which had already been found in the Pacific) which has *a distinctly hinged valve* which can be opened and closed exactly like the valves of such a mollusk as the oyster or clam. But the evolutionists have continued to deny that these structures are anything more than some of nature's morphological tricks calculated to deceive the unskillful. And they resolutely declare that the ascidians, so far from being related to the mollusks, are really degenerate vertebrates. Verily the ways of morphologists are past finding out.

We have already mentioned various instances where organs of flight are found on animals widely unrelated to each other, structures which must have been independently evolved, if they have been evolved at all. Willey mentions two other very striking examples of this sort, the *Exocoetus,* or flying herring, a true teleost fish, which is strikingly like the flying gurnard, though the latter belongs to an entirely different family. " Both of these genera occur in the Mediterranean as well as in the Indian Ocean, and are totally different from each other, not only in systematic position but in external forms." But though thus dissimilar in a general way, each has the same elongation and expansion of the pectoral fins which enable the animal to use this organ as a parachute, which, as Willey says, is a very exceptional modification " which has been acquired independently within the limits of two very distinct families." And he adds that it is indeed " remarkable to find such strictly homologous organs as the pectoral fins of Teleostean fishes modified in a virtually identical manner to perform a special and exceptional function, whose transformation is nevertheless not homogenetic but homoplastic " (op. cit., p. 89). These last two terms mean that this structure is alike in appearance but unlike in origin. We have already seen that such terms embalm too much evolutionary theory.

Charles Darwin devoted considerable attention to the electric organs of fishes, and said that " it is impossible to conceive by what steps these wondrous organs have been produced." He admitted that in several instances these organs cannot be supposed to have had a common origin. In some species these electric organs are in the head, while in others they are situated in the tail; and it is thus quite evident that they could not have had a common origin. Romanes tried to account for these organs in the rays, but confessed that the difficulty of accounting for them was so great " that if there were many other cases of the like kind to be met with in nature, I should myself at once allow that the theory of natural selection would have to be discarded." In this he recognized that the difficulty is vastly increased by the fact that these organs have had several independent origins. Not only do we find these organs in the well-known genus *Torpedo*, belonging to the rays or skates, but also in the electric eel of South America and the astonishing electric catfish of the rivers of Africa, the latter of which grows to a length of three feet. In the latter animal the electrical apparatus " differs absolutely from that of all other fishes, being derived from the integument, belonging to the glandular system, and surrounding the whole body with a thick coat of grease or gelatinous substance " (T. W. Bridge). This latter fish is called *raad* by the Arabs, the name meaning *thunder,* a tribute to the very powerful shock which this fish can generate. And in all of these three instances the difficulty of accounting for the electric equipment is greatly increased by the fact that " in each case, as pointed out by Dr. D. S. Jordan, closely related species show no trace of the electric endowment " (Arthur Willey).

Of course, in these instances as in all other similar lines, the greatest difficulty is in trying to imagine how these structures could have had their first minute useless beginnings. For it seems to be an insuperable difficulty for the theory of natural selection that these organs had to be preserved for a long time in their rudimentary stages when they were absolutely useless. It would seem that natural selection ought to have eliminated these useless structures almost as soon as they appeared, thus allowing them no chance to become functional and useful. But this problem only becomes greater when we are driven to say that very similar useless structures have originated time and time again, and also have repeatedly persisted through the rudimentary or useless stage until they became useful to the organism.

The origin of the placenta and its many related and complicated structures presents a very great problem for the evolutionist to solve. The special difficulties connected with this problem are of a technical nature and need not concern us here. But it is worthy of note that a true allantoic placenta is found in the bandicoots of Australia, Tasmania, and New Guinea. This makes it necessary for the evolutionist to say, either that the marsupials have descended from a stock which already had an allantoic placenta, all but the bandicoots having *subsequently lost* this structure, or to say that this structure has had an independent development among the two widely separated groups of the mammalia. Neither horn of this dilemma presents a very encouraging problem for the evolutionist.

The problem of the origin of the organs among the higher vertebrates which secrete milk for the young, presents difficulties of its own, for here we have a structure indispensable to the plan of mammalian life, but not rationally and structurally connected with the viviparous method of generation. That is, there does not seem to be any anatomical or structural relationship between the mammae and the production of the young in a uterus; and yet either of these structures would be absolutely useless without the other.

But the secretion of milk has an interest all its own, independent of its connection with the placental method of reproduction. It has been pointed out that pigeons, during the breeding season, secrete a large quantity of a milky fluid in their crops, this fluid being of a grey colour and forming a curd by coagulation with acids. This " pigeon's milk," as it is called, is mixed with food in the crop and is fed to the young by regurditation, being of a very nutritious character and well adapted to the nourishment of the young birds.

But one is astonished at finding a somewhat analogous secretion in the uterus of viviparous rays. In at least three distinct genera, the sting-rays, the eagle-rays, and the bat-rays, the young are nourished before birth by a milky secretion which is produced by glandular structures on the inner surface of the uterine wall, a funnel-like structure carrying this milk into the pharynx or throat of the embryo fish. Not only is a structure provided to *guide the milk into the throat* of the young embryo, but muscles in the wall of the uterus by their contraction *squeeze the milk out*. This production of milk on the part of these fishes is without doubt a most remarkable parallel to the corresponding phenomena in mammals, even though the structures producing it are in great contrast with the mammalian structures. But how any or all of these structures could have originated by natural selection or by any other method of evolution, quite passes my powers of imagination.

" Every system of organs throughout the animal kingdom will be found to yield abundant instances of convergence," or examples of structures quite independently evolved, as Willey declares. He further tells us that the degrees of convergence are endless and constitute " a dominant factor in morphology " (pp. 91, 107, 130). " The influence of convergence in evolution has been wide-spread, deep-seated, and intimate, more so than is generally recognized. What may appear to be a brilliant discovery of morphological affinity may in reality be an equally brilliant demonstration of the no less important and interesting phenomenon of morphological convergence " (pp. 168, 169). And this illustrious author, whose work on convergence is an encyclopedia of examples along this line, closes with the significant statement that these examples tend to break down all the former land-marks of homology, and that " hardly one universal criterion of strict homology can be mentioned which would pass muster in a critical examination " (p. 170).

X

Among the wealth of illustrations which might be presented here, we can select only a few more. All of the higher animals have, of course, special organs for the digestion of the food. But while we are not surprised at the presence of a stomach in all of them, we are naturally surprised at finding in addition such a peculiar and specialized organ as a gizzard in such widely different animals as birds, crocodiles, ant-eaters, and several kinds of fishes. The ancient dinosaurs also seem to have had gizzards, what have been identified as gizzard stones having been found within the skeleton in a few instances. Of course, the toothless ant-eaters would naturally need a gizzard to grind up their food, quite as much so as toothless birds. But in the case of the fishes we have an almost identical structure in several widely separated families, such as the grey mullet, the red mullet, the so-called gillaroo or " gizzard trout," and the " gizzard shad." Willey gives a comparison between these structures in the mullet and the shad, and adds,

"Here, then, we have two fishes belonging to widely separated families, though pursuing similar habits, and presenting independently an identical modification of the pyloric division of the stomach. I confess that at first acquaintance with this case I began to distrust my own eyes" (p. 110).

He goes on to say that these shads and mullets, so widely different in other respects, have also adipose or fatty eyelids in common, as well as pyloric gizzards. And he adds,

"In both of these cases, as well as in that of the pectoral fins of the flying fishes, we have anatomically identical structures arising independently from a common origin. Facts of this nature apparently take the ground away from any intelligible conception of homology—but only apparently" (p. 111).

However, I take it that these last three words, " *but only apparently,*" are merely a gesture of protest against the profound doubt of the whole evolution theory which is naturally inspired by such a destruction of all the laws of homology. This author still maintains his belief in the general doctrine of organic evolution, although such facts certainly seem to remove all scientific basis for regarding homology as of any evidential value in favour of this general doctrine.

The mechanism of breathing would offer us many instructive comparisons. For example, the presence of almost identical breathing organs, or tracheae, in the insects and the arachnids, led scientists for many years to class these groups together under the general name of Tracheata, in contradistinction to the aquatic arthropods which were called Branchiata. But within modern times it has been declared that the insects and arachnids are very widely apart; and thus that their similar breathing organs, or tracheae, must have had separate origins. Accordingly these similar organs are now said to be different, from the standpoint of morphology, and not at all truly homologous, though they are identically similar both in their histologic structure and in their physiologic functions. Even among the arachnoids we are told that the tracheae " have had at least a twofold origin, namely, from lung-books and from ectodermal tendons " (Willey). Thus we are compelled by the theory of evolution to say that " similarity of structure in the fully developed tracheae does not mean similarity of origin " (Purcell).

Willey says that tracheal tubes have replaced lung-books " at least twice," in the two-lunged spiders and in the " false scorpions;" also in the land operculates, or mollusks with an operculum, and in the *Pulmonata,* or mollusks without an operculum, as Helix and Pupa, which belong to an entirely different order. This makes essentially *four times* that these very similar breathing organs have been developed *independently* among these invertebrates, if we are to believe the evolution theory.

If we descend to the histology or the study of the cellular structure of some of the lower animals, we find some very interesting comparisons. A few years ago the theory was propounded that an identity of histologic or cellular structure might be considered proof of identity of origin. But there are very many instances where this will not hold good. For instance, in certain annelid worms we find a certain type of kidneys, or nephridia, constructed of characteristic "flame-cells," so-called; while in the amphioxus we have nephridia or kidneys composed of the very same kind of cells. E. S. Goodrich, who made this discovery, argued for a common ancestry for these widely separated creatures, and said that if these similar structures " could be shown to have been independently evolved, we should have to give up structural resemblance as a guide to homology." But Willey contends that these structures have *certainly been independently evolved,* and says that these are only examples of histogenetic convergence, or independent development of an identical cellular structure.

Willey gives other examples of a similar nature, and says that it would " be possible to multiply examples of histological parallelism to an almost unlimited extent " (p. 166). He shows that this parallelism in cellular structure, in widely separated animals that cannot be spoken of as having had a common origin, is only similar to that convergence or parallelism of or-

gans in widely separated animals which likewise cannot have been of a common descent. He admits that
" most morphological arguments work both ways;"
and on another page he says that a comparison of this
sort, perhaps, no matter which structure we compare
with the other, " leads round in a vicious circle to the
same goal, namely, the point from which we started "
(p. 114). He further admits that " it is a very good
thing to have a guiding idea in morphology and to follow it out, but at the best it can lead only to a sub-
jective conclusion " (p. 165). I agree fully.

XI

Having thus seen that almost innumerable examples
could be given of organs, tissues, and cellular structures in widely separated animals where these forms
could not possibly have had a common origin, we begin
to see that morphology is of very little value in proving
genetic relationships. But we may proceed to study
the instincts and habits of animals, and we shall see
the same rule applying here.

For example, there is a very remarkable similarity
in the habits and instincts of the various social insects,
such as the termites, the ants, the bees, and the wasps.
The termites resemble ants so closely in their mode of
life and in their social organization that in the tropical
countries they are usually known as white ants, though,
as Willey says, " they are not ants and are not always
white." The reader is probably familiar with the three
kinds of bees which live together in the same hive or
colony, namely, the queen, the workers, and the drones.
Among many of the ants there are several other or
different classes or castes. While among the termites,
as a recent writer has worked it out, there are several

dozen distinct orders or castes. The termites do not keep slaves, or milk-producing insects, as do some of the ants, but the social differentiation into workers, soldiers, kings, and queens is the same among the termites as among the ants. The termites also keep certain other insects in their homes as " guests," which often resemble their hosts in outward appearance to a very remarkable degree. Some of these " guests " thus entertained among both the ants and the termites are harmless or even friendly; while others are distinctly harmful, and feed upon their unsuspecting hosts when the latter are caught off guard.

The many lessons to be learned from the instincts of these social insects are too numerous to be mentioned here. The fact that the working bees are always descended from a queen mother who never gathered a drop of honey in her life and from a lazy drone that hangs around the hive as a " cake-eater," without ever doing a tap of useful work, is proof enough that in this case at least the effects of use and disuse are not transmitted to the offspring. How does the young worker bee know from the beginning what to do and how to do it, in the way of gathering honey, making comb, and the hundred other duties connected with the life of the hive? These workers have peculiar structures on their legs, often called " baskets," for carrying pollen. Several other structures might be mentioned which are peculiar to the workers. Thus there are both structures and instincts which are strictly confined to the worker, not being found in either the queen mother or the drone father; hence the worker's ancestors never had them. It is impossible to imagine how these structures or these instincts could have been built up by inheritance from the long line of queens and drones which are this worker's ancestors, for these ancestors *never possessed them*. Hence these structures and instincts cannot be called " hereditary " except by an accommodated use of the word; and I can see no possible way by which these peculiarities in the worker can be accounted for on any theory of evolution.

But essentially the same difficulty confronts us in the cases of the wasps, the ants, and the termites. Certain castes among all of these social insects have very striking peculiarities of structure and of instincts which are *confined to these castes and which the fathers and mothers have never possessed*. And if the evolution theory be true, these four groups of the social insects must have developed *each quite independently* this most astonishing propensity of having certain castes or classes among them which seem to violate all the laws of heredity, by showing structures and instincts which are never found in the direct line of the ancestry. I do not believe it.

In still another way we are confronted with an insuperable difficulty in explaining the instincts among these social colonies. For it is not one instinct alone that we have to account for; the instincts involved are literally hundreds in number. The hive is a very complex social organization; and if a single break occurs in the social structure the existence of the entire colony is at stake. No bee can live alone by himself. Neither worker, nor drone, nor queen could possibly make a living for himself or herself. They must exist together as a colony, or they will all perish. In the case of many human beings who live together in a social life, the habits and needs are many of them very artificial, and could very easily be dispensed with.

Not so with these wonderful insect societies. There is no single instinct or habit among the bees but is imperative, and absolutely indispensable for the very existence of the colony. These instincts could never have been evolved one by one; they must all exist in their totality and in their perfection, or the colony could not exist. Thus we see the impossibility of accounting for these habits by any theory of organic evolution.

But these latter remarks are just as true of the social wasps, the ants, and the termites, as of the bees. And when we see that these social instincts and habits must, according to the evolution theory, have been developed *quite independently* among all these various classes of insects, it is not too much to say that such a theory taxes our credulity beyond endurance.

The swarming habit shown by several kinds of annelid worms is very astonishing. For example, the palolo (*Eunice viridis*), which lives at a depth of six or eight feet among the coral rocks near Samoa and Fiji, is quite similar in structure to the various "rockworms" which are found around various parts of the British Isles and in the Western Mediterranean. The remarkable thing about the palolo is the absolute regularity with which it swarms or reproduces. At midnight, on the last quarter of the October moon, no matter what the weather may be like, fair or foul, calm or hurricane, uncounted millions of these creatures rise to the surface, where they remain for a few hours, going through a process of dividing or budding, a sexual form of reproduction which is equivalent to spawning among the higher forms of life. The palolo never fails to appear at exactly the right time, for it keeps astronomical time; and as the natives catch these worms and eat them as a great delicacy, as well as the fish which follow them and prey upon them, the occasions for the appearance of the palolo are eagerly awaited, and can be predicted with the same certainty as Christmas or the fourth of July.

The dividing or segmentation which these worms go through simultaneously at the surface, results in the death of the old individuals, and the formation of buds or minute segments which, like so many eggs, sink to the bottom, and grow and mature into full-grown specimens by the time another year has rolled around. If a few individual specimens are placed in a glass jar and carefully examined, it will be seen that they also break up into segments at the same time that this segmentation occurs among their companions in the ocean.

With what astonishment do we watch these creatures in the jar, almost at a given signal, as it were, breaking into pieces, just as their comrades are doing in the sea, and just as their ancestors have done from time immemorial. These budding segments, which sink together to the bottom of the water, have surely a wonderful inheritance, if inheritance it be, received from their ancestors. " Their fathers and mothers are already dead; and they, on the third quarter of the ensuing October moon, at the hour of midnight, will rise to the surface, commingle a few hours, and at 8 A. M. they will also die, and the next generation will sink, even as they, to the mysterious home of the palolo."

It seems preposterous to suggest an evolutionary explanation for such instincts and habits as these. How could such a habit have arisen in the first instance? In the case of the palolo worm there are absolutely *no survivors* from one year to another; hence, how can

the young palolo have *acquired such a habit as this?*
Moreover, how is it that all the acts of this cycle of
life always come around on time, even to the day and
the hour, and all this in the case of uncounted millions
of individuals seemingly acting together in absolute
unison?

To add to our surprise, we find that very similar
habits of swarming occur at another time of year, June
and July, among the Atlantic palolos; while a Japanese
palolo, belonging to what is called an entirely different
family, goes through a very similar performance in the
nights following the new and the full moon in October
and November. However, in the latter case the sexual
segments are confined to the *anterior* portion of the
animal, while in the Samoan palolo it is the *posterior*
part of the body which is broken in pieces. Thus the
difficulty of accounting for one of these instances becomes multiplied when we see that it occurs in several
forms which apparently are not closely related to each
other.

We have space to mention only one or two more examples. We have many kinds of fishes which agree
in the curious habit of carrying on the incubation of
the eggs in the mouth. Thus we have the *Arius* of
Ceylon, a kind of cat-fish, in which a dozen or fifteen
eggs half an inch in diameter are held in the mouth of
the male until they are hatched. In this case the
opening of the oesophagus is constricted and almost
closed for the time that this incubation goes on, while
the mouth and the pharynx are greatly enlarged so as
to form a spacious brood-pouch. The same structure
and habits are also recorded for a different species in
South America.

A toad-like batrachian, of Chile, South America, has

two openings in the floor of the mouth, in the case of the male, which at the breeding season become enlarged and extend like large brood-pouches back to the pubic region. In these pouches the eggs are incubated. Thus we have an almost identical structure in these fishes and in these amphibians.

Incubation of the eggs in a fold of the skin is another curious method of caring for the eggs, which is seen in the case of the pipe-fishes, where it occurs in the male in certain families, while in other families the same office is performed by the female. In a certain cat-fish of Guiana, the *Aspredo,* the female carries the eggs attached to the spongy skin of the belly, in much the same way as the well-known Surinam toad, *Pipa,* carries her eggs on the back. But a still closer analogy to the fish just mentioned is the case of a frog in Ceylon, where the eggs, about twenty in number, are found fastened to the abdomen of the female, adhering together so as to form a flat disc. The midwife toad of Europe, *Alytes obstetricans,* has a very similar habit of carrying the eggs, except that in this case it is the male which acts as guardian for the eggs. In other animals still more remote in point of relationship, we have this same method of brood-nursing, as for example in the case of a certain kind of amphibious water-bug, which has the habit of carrying the eggs in the form of a disc cemented upon the back of the male, which are placed there by the female.

XII

In his presidential address before the Botanical Section, at the Liverpool meeting of the British Association (1923), Prof. A. G. Tansley dwelt upon the increasing doubt among modern botanists regarding the origin of many organs which were formerly thought to be homogenetic, or of common origin by descent. Thus we find that the botanists are meeting with the same difficulties which have so long troubled the zoologists. Many quotations might be given here to show that these newer ideas have affected the botanists in much the same way as they have the zoologists, by tending to throw all of the old evolutionary ideas into confusion. Prof. F. O. Bower, of the University of Glasgow, says that " at the present moment we seem to have reached a phase of negation in respect " to the former ideas that we could trace out the evolutionary pedigree of our modern floras. " The whole of this branch of botany," he says, " seems to leave the great majority of the younger botanists cold " (*Nature*, March 8, 1924).

From all this we see that botany as well as zoology has reached an *impasse*. Each of these sciences has been making it its chief business to trace out evolutionary lines of descent for the modern living forms with which it has been dealing. But in the closer examination of the organs and the embryonic development of these forms, botany as well as zoology has found itself up at the end of a blind alley; and each of these sciences is now looking about in bewilderment seeking some way out.

XIII

If now we attempt to gather up the conclusions to be extracted from the series of facts which we have been studying, it seems to me that *morphology completely fails us as a guide in attempting to trace out genetic relationships*. There is scarcely a single structure in the whole animal kingdom which cannot be found almost duplicated in two or more kinds of animals widely separated from each other, where it is impossible to imagine a community of descent, and where, on any theory of evolution, we must say that these structures have been independently evolved. It thus appears that homology is a chimera, when we undertake to use it to prove evolution or genetic relationships. As Willey admits, " Hardly one universal criterion of strict homology can be mentioned which would pass muster in a critical examination." Morphological comparisons, or even alleged homologies, may be very convenient and very useful, from the standpoint of classification and of study. These methods enable us to make comparisons between the various kinds of animals, and we may in this way organize our knowledge into a science. But if we are to maintain any clearness of thought, in other words, if we do not allow ourselves to become fooled or bewildered by the tools of classification which we employ, we will have to acknowledge that all our systems of classification are mere artificial schemes, simply convenient intellectual devices for organizing our knowledge into a science. But to permit the final products of such a classification to deceive us into thinking that we have thereby shown how one kind of animal has developed into another, is to show a decided lack of mental clearness. We might similarly arrange all the various kinds of dogs in a serial line from the wee toy dogs of Paris up to the mastiff or the St. Bernard; but only a fool would argue from this that the latter breeds had been derived from the former. Indeed, one might arrange all the various automobiles now in existence, from the Ford runabout to the Packard or the Pierce-Arrow; and yet no one would suppose that this arrangement really showed anything in the way of genetic descent; the Dodge or the Chevrolet is not the missing link between the Ford and the Packard.

In short, we must say that the whole morphological argument which was so strongly used by Darwin and his followers, which has been so long employed to show how the higher kinds of animals have evolved, is a snare and a delusion. It does not at all prove what the evolutionist has said that it proves; and if we are to maintain clear habits of thinking we must say that morphological comparisons are utterly useless in showing genetic relationships, except, of course, where the whole structure of an animal is like that of another, as in the case of the dog, which has quite evidently been derived from the wolf, or as in the case of the common domestic cat and the various kinds of wild cats, which have evidently been derived from the same primary ancestors as the lions, tigers, and leopards.

BIBLIOGRAPHY

Cambridge Natural History, 10 vols.; 1909.

Flower (W. H.) and Lydekker (R.), *Mammals Living and Extinct;* 1891.

Mivart, St. G., *The Genesis of Species;* 1871.

Osborn, H. F., *Paleontology,* in *Encycl. Brit.,* Vol. XX, pp. 579-591.

Willey, Arthur, *Convergence in Evolution;* 1911.

VII

THE DEVELOPING EMBRYO

I

EVERY one of the higher animals has started from a single cell, the fertilized *ovum*, formed by the union of two cells, the matured ovum and the sperm, or spermatozoon. To understand the development of this fertilized ovum into the mature animal, it will be necessary to consider briefly the characters and behaviour of cells in general.

The higher types of both plants and animals are composed of multitudes of cells, each of which may be compared to some of the lower forms of life, such as the amoeba, which consists of but a single cell. A typical cell is surrounded by a cell wall, is composed of a mass of protoplasm, which is granular in structure, and constitutes what Huxley called the physical basis of life. It contains a well-marked portion called the *nucleus*, with other structures which are quite characteristic of it. The detailed description of the cell is not essential for us; but we must note how cells multiply.

Ordinary cell division, by which one cell divides and becomes two cells, is called *mitosis*. During this highly complicated process of mitosis, the nucleus divides, certain characteristic structures called the *chromosomes* appear out of a more or less undifferentiated portion called the chromatin. These chromosomes arrange themselves at right angles to the axis between the two nuclei, and then each chromosome splits lengthwise, one-half going to the one end or side of the cell and the other half going to the other. A constriction between these two portions of the cell now takes place, and thus the one cell has become two. With some further growth and maturation, each of these cells is now a fully matured individual unit, ready to take its part in the functions of the organism to which it belongs.

The cells composing one of the higher animals may be divided into two general classes, (1) somatic cells and (2) germ or reproductive cells.

The *somatic* or body cells perform the various functions of muscular action, responding to stimuli, and the many complicated processes connected with metabolism and growth. These cells are grouped together into what we call tissues, groups of tissues comprising an organ; thus forming the muscles, nerves and other structures of man and animals; and the leaves, branches and roots of plants.

The *germ* cells do not take any part in the routine work of the body, such as the digestion of food or the various bodily functions. They constitute a sort of cellular aristocracy, with one work only to perform, namely, to serve as the origin of other new individuals like the individual in which they are located. These germ cells are not produced by the somatic cell; rather should we say that the somatic or body cells are produced by the germ cells. In this view of the matter, the old problem of which came first the hen or the egg, is easily solved; the egg produces the hen and other eggs. These germ cells are protected and nourished by the somatic cells, and are safely cared for in special organs. But the germ cells are a class apart by themselves; they preserve their individuality, and never unite with the body cells.

The female germ cell, called the *ovum,* goes through a process of what is called *maturation,* during which the number of chromosomes which it contains becomes reduced one-half. It may now become fertilized by one of the male sperm cells entering it and uniting with it, this male or sperm cell having already gone through a similar process of reduction, so that it also carries only the half number of chromosomes. By the union of these two germ cells, the original or normal number of the chromosomes is restored. These chromosomes are now regarded as the carriers of all the various hereditary qualities. All of the cells of any certain species of animal have each the same number of chromosomes, the body cells having the same number as the germ cells. The cells of the frog have fourteen, certain snails have thirty-two; while for man the number is variously stated as twenty-four or forty-eight.

The newly fertilized ova of an elephant, a dog, a woman, or a whale, would be essentially all alike. Not even the highest powers of the microscope are sufficient to show any noticeable differences between them, except in size and in the number of the chromosomes. This only means that any one of the higher animals starts from a single fertilized germ cell which is to all appearances exactly like the germ cell from which any other animal originates. Thus, as they all start alike, *there must be many constant characteristics in the early stages of their development wherein they would seem to run parallel to each other*. Each of these fertilized ova will first divide into halves, each half being called a daughter cell. These two daughter cells next divide, making four; a further division makes eight; and this division is continued until a greater or lesser number of cells is produced, the number varying with the kind of animal under consideration.

The process of division of the germ cell is called *cleavage;* and when this process has continued for a number of times, the mass of the cells will perhaps now look like a mulberry, a sphere composed of a great many individual cells.[1] Presently the cleavage cells arrange themselves so as to form a structure more like a hollow sphere, the cleavage cells themselves merely composing the wall of this sphere. This is called the *blastoderm* or *blastula* stage of development, and this stage is likewise common to all of the higher kinds of animals. Next a portion of the blastoderm cell-layer bends inward, producing a groove or small depression, resulting in forming two portions of the blastoderm layer, the inner portion which has sunken in being called the *endoblast,* and the other portion which has preserved its original form being called the *ectoblast.* When this stage of development is completed it is called the *gastrula* stage; and it is characterized by a double walled layer around a central cavity. This gastrula stage is also common to all the higher animals; that is, the human embryo, with that of an elephant, or a dog, or a fish, each goes through its gastrula stage.

[1] NOTE.—If the cleavage cells are made to separate from one another in the two-cell or the four-cell stage, each of these cells will then go on to develop into an entire animal of smaller size than the normal. In this way two complete individuals have been produced from a single egg of a starfish, a sea-urchin, an amphioxus, and of several other kinds of invertebrates. Various theoretical explanations have been offered for these remarkable facts.

In the case of most of the higher animals, the development of the embryo goes on within the body of the mother until it becomes a highly complex organism, composed of many tissues and organs. In the case of the birds, this development takes place within the egg, which is outside the body of the mother. But the development in all cases is essentially the same. The development is continuous from the stage of the germ cell to the mature animal; and whether this development goes on inside or outside of an egg structure, it is a regular and uninterrupted process of development.

If we could examine the cells composing the embryo in any of its early stages, whether in the cleavage stage, the blastoderm stage, or even in the gastrula stage, we should find that these cells are all apparently alike; there seems to be little or no differentiation between them. But from the gastrula stage onward there is a gradual differentiation of the cells into distinct groups to form the various kinds of tissues; these tissues become grouped together into organs and the various parts of the body, resulting in the development of the mature individual. Since a horse, a pigeon, a grasshopper, a starfish, and a man all start alike from a single fertilized cell, *it necessarily follows that they will run parallel to one another in several of their early stages of development.* Any other method would be a whimsical disregard of the principle of economy and expediency in nature.

We may make a comparison between their parallelism in development and the directions pursued by various lines of railway running out from such a center as Chicago. All the eastern roads continue parallel to each other for a long distance out of the city; but gradually some of them turn to the south, others to the north, while still others keep on due eastward. And it necessarily follows that the several roads which lead to Montreal, New York, or Boston hold more closely to the same general direction for a much longer distance, than is the case with those roads which ultimately turn to Georgia or Florida.

In the same way, we might expect that any two of the higher animals, as a man and a gorilla, or even a man and a dog, or a man and a horse, would show many more resemblances to each other in their embryonic development, than would be the case between a man and a starfish, or even between a man and a turtle. Contrastedly, we would expect that an insect and a vertebrate would begin to diverge from one another more early in their development; while two insects, as a beetle and a grasshopper, or any two vertebrates, as a fish and a dog, would not begin to diverge from each other so soon. In other words, all of the developing vertebrates may be spoken of as diverging in one general direction, and the invertebrates in another general direction; but the various members of the vertebrates will journey along together for a considerable time, and only as they come to stages further along toward maturity are we able clearly to distinguish one kind from another. All this is of the very nature of things; it could not well be otherwise, if nature is efficient and economical in her processes of embryonic development. And yet for nearly a hundred years evolutionists have excitedly pointed to these facts as proofs of their theory that man and the higher mammals have all gone through the lower stages of life in their evolutionary development millions of years ago.

II

When the general facts of embryonic development were first made known about a hundred years ago, those who were inclined toward the evolution theory pointed out these facts of parallelism as very significant. It was claimed that one of the higher animals in its embryonic development always passes through a very rapid and very much condensed recapitulation of the history which its species has passed through in the course of its evolution through a long series of gradually developing ancestors. This is the well-known *recapitulation theory,* which during the latter part of the nineteenth century was considered one of the strongest arguments in favour of the theory of organic evolution. This theory was much employed by Haeckel and his followers; by them it was exalted into an alleged " biogenetic law," or principle of all life; and under the guidance of such men as Louis Agassiz, E. D. Cope, and Alpheus Hyatt, embryonic comparisons have for two generations or more been used as the chief key to determine the best or " natural " method of classifying the various genera and species, the fossils as well as the living ones.

In harmony with what has been given above, the human embryo very early shows traces of a vertebral column, terminating in an enlarged bulb which ultimately becomes the brain. It should be remembered that during its entire development the embryo is strictly dependent on its own resources; for it receives neither blood supply nor nerve stimulation of any kind from the mother, who simply acts as its guardian or nurse; hence this central nervous system, with its apparently undue size of the brain, is the very essential foundation stage for all of its future growth. In this stage the embryo is very small; but under a magnifying glass it is seen to be divided into several lobes with what looks much like a " tail," the latter constricted into a series of thirty-two segments, each of the latter being the start for one of the future vertebrae, or of the nerve-centers contained within these vertebrae. Though still very small, the embryo is seen to be curved upon its ventral surface[1] in the shape of a semicircle. Two dark spots are seen on the sides of one of the anterior lobes, these spots marking the locations of the future eyes.

In this stage the thorax and the abdomen have not been formed, and of course none of the viscera or internal organs have yet started. From about the middle of the segmented hind part, familiarly called the " tail," there develops a system of vessels which terminate in a globular mass, these vessels furnishing the nutriment for the growing embryo. Close in front of the bulb which marks the cerebellum, under the bulb composing the forebrain, are seen several incomplete arches with a corresponding number of clefts or depressions between them, these structures arising from the sides and uniting at the median line in front. When the embryo becomes more developed, the upper one of these arches forms the upper jaw; the second forms the lower jaw; between them, when the two sides of the organs have united is the oral or mouth cavity. The others eventually go to form the organs of the neck, the roots of the tongue, and the larynx.

---

[1] NOTE.—In contrast with this forward or ventral curvature of the vertebrate embryo, it should be noted that the embryo of many of the invertebrates is curved backwards, or dorsally. How could both of these methods indicate the same ancestry, if the recapitulation theory be true?

These parts have been called *branchial arches,* because of their fancied resemblance to the arches of certain fishes which support the gills. By Haeckel and others the clefts or depressions between them were called " gill-slits," though actual openings into the pharynx are never formed in the human embryo; and evolutionists never become tired of pointing to them as proof that man in the long ago passed through a stage resembling that of a fish. But it should be expressly noted that these embryonic arches do not take any part in producing the respiratory organs in man, as the true branchial arches do in the fish. In the light of what is now known about this part of embryology, it may be stated with confidence that *these so-called arches and clefts are the very natural and necessary structural preparation for the growth of the organs which ultimately develop from them*. Any fancied resemblance between these structures and the gill-slits of elasmobranch fishes is merely the product of a highly inventive imagination. Inaccurate or even deliberately false diagrams of these parts have been peddled around from one textbook to another, materially assisting in this misconception, Haeckel's inventions having been one of the chief supports of this propaganda.

Frankly, it is quite discouraging to see that Vernon Kellogg, in his latest work, *Evolution the Way of Man* (1924), dwells long and earnestly on this argument from " recapitulation," gill-clefts and all, and says that these " recapitulation " features of the embryo constitute " one of the strongest of the evidences of evolution " (p. 54). I had thought that modern science had definitely outgrown this whimsical explanation of the structures found in the human embryo, and that the exposure of the methods used by Haeckel in this connection had brought the whole thing into a state where common sense and accuracy would again have the right of way over whimsicality and misrepresentation.

III

Many of the alleged instances of vestigial organs in man, as adduced by the evolutionists, are trivial and childish, while others are completely false as to fact. I do not know of a single instance that ought not properly to be classed under the one head or the other.

Among the trivial ones may be mentioned the muscles of the ears, of the scalp, and of the coccyx, with the coccyx itself, which has been asserted to be the relic of a tail. Arguments based on such examples are trivial in the extreme; and would never have been used in this connection, if Charles Darwin had not set the example. If the theologians of the Middle Ages were addicted to hair splitting and word twisting, the evolutionists have merely changed the form, but not the habit.

Among the organs which were once said to be useless relics of the past, may be mentioned the thyroid gland, the pineal gland, and the vermiform appendix. The thyroid used to be called a useless heirloom; but with the advance in a knowledge of physiological processes, we now know that it serves a very essential function in keeping us all from becoming cretins. Indeed, the mistake made by evolutionists regarding the thyroid was recognized by Huxley, who said: "The recent discovery of the important part played by the thyroid gland should be a warning to all speculators about useless organs."

But this warning was unheeded; for in 1919, Sir

Arthur Keith, in his presidential address before the Anthropological Section of the British Association for the Advancement of Science, had this to say:

"We have hitherto regarded the pineal gland, little bigger than a wheat grain and buried deeply in the brain, as a mere useless vestige of a median or parietal eye, derived from some distant human ancestor in whom that eye was functional; but on the clinical and experimental evidence now rapidly accumulating we must assign to it a place in the machinery which controls the growth of the body" (*Smithsonian Report,* 1919; p. 448).

Another portion of the human anatomy which is often spoken of as a vestige or relic from some previous form of animal life, is the vermiform appendix, a tubular structure about the size of a short lead pencil. Evolutionists claim that this worm-like appendage is the vestigial remains of the much elongated caecum of the herbivorous animals. This vermiform appendix is found also in the anthropoid apes and in most other herbivorous animals; but in man it has often been regarded as a useless or even a dangerous relic of the past. Among civilized peoples this organ often gives a good deal of trouble; but it is significant that among people who live more naturally, the organ never gives any trouble whatever; and we may well suppose that it has a useful function to perform, though it is not well understood just what its function really is. The appendix is composed largely of lymphoid tissue, in common with the spleen, the thymus, and the tonsils; and any of these can apparently be removed without causing any particular harm to the rest of the body. However, we do know that all of these organs serve as the factories or points of origin of large quantities of the white blood-cells.

It also appears that these lymphoid tissues, including the appendix, act as filters or obstructions to foreign particles, such as disease germs, and even to chemical poisons, in their passage toward the general circulation system. It may be safely asserted that the appendix has a useful work to perform, and that in the normal condition of the body it not only would never be of any trouble necessitating its surgical removal, but would assist in maintaining the normal tone of the body. The old notion that it is a relic of a former stage of man's existence, a useless and dangerous heirloom which has persisted in man's body when it is not wanted and not needed, is merely a part of the alleged evidence in favour of the evolution theory which has no substantial foundation in actual fact.

Another class of organs which present rather more plausible arguments for organic evolution, are the genuine rudimentary organs, such as the upper incisor teeth of foetal calves, which never break through the gums but are resorbed; the minute traces of hind limbs in the pythons, boas, and some other serpents; the rudimentary teeth of certain whales which never cut through the gums. Structures like these are quite common through the whole range of the animal kingdom. The trace of a wing which we find in the apteryx of Australia, may be of the same nature as the rudimentary eyes of the blind fish in caves; for it is evident that the latter are descended from ancestors which once had functional eyes. But Mendelism has thrown much light on the possibilities of such structures; for Morgan has produced several types of blind flies, and also of wingless ones; and he got these types, not by a long series of gradual reductions, but by a single mutation.

But genetic experiments have shown that we can, by the proper methods, again bring out these suppressed characters or structures, so that the descendants of these eyeless or wingless varieties will have fully functional eyes and wings. And although we cannot conduct similar experiments in the case of the whale, or perhaps even in that of the apteryx or the domestic cattle, it is quite reasonable to suppose that the same general principles of Mendelian segregation hold true throughout the entire animal kingdom. Hence if we could perform the proper breeding experiments, we might be able to bring out into full functional activity many, or possibly all, of these curious rudimentary organs which we find so wide-spread through the various types of animals, and also of plants.

Thus these rudimentary organs are no longer a puzzle; least of all do they render any support to the evolution hypothesis. They do show the possibilities of change or variation, and are thus an argument against the older ideas of the absolute " fixity " of " species;" but they give no encouragement to the doctrine of the evolution of all animal forms from a single protozoic ancestor. In the light of what we have brought out above, these rudimentary organs (foetal teeth, etc.) might all be classed with the stumps of tails in certain dogs or cats, or the traces of horns on hornless cattle. That is, they are only visible, surface manifestations of latent characters which can always be brought out into functional activity by appropriate methods of breeding. In many houses we see sets of electric wires which are never used; they were inserted there for a possible contingency that might require them. In a similar way, nature has made provision for many structures that may not be used very much, sometimes are never used at all, under the present environment of these animals or plants; whereas under other environments in the long ago they may have been useful, or they may again become of use when the real proper environment of these animals or plants is again restored.

IV

We have already mentioned the recapitulation theory which was so much overworked by Haeckel, the self-appointed evangelist for making Darwinism popular in Germany. This theory of recapitulation has had its own vicissitudes, and its standing has greatly declined among real scientists, though it is still being used by the more ardent advocates of the evolution doctrine in much the same way as it was used by Haeckel.

It will be in order to deal, first, with the subject historically.

In the story of the death of Absalom, it will be remembered that Ahimaaz, the son of Zadok, was determined to run with a message when as yet he really had no tidings ready. Too often in the early history of scientific discoveries a theory has become popular when it had only the slenderest pretext of accurate knowledge. Time and again the theories which have misled the world and which have been widely heralded as disproving the Bible, have been broadcasted when only the merest smattering of knowledge was really known. It was in this way that the recapitulation theory had its beginnings. Lorenzo Oken, an *a priori* philosopher and theorizer, in 1805 and subsequently, published an interpretation of embryonic development in which he said that the ovum of one of the higher animals passes through or repeats the forms of all the classes of animals below it, making a repetition of the story of creation in its own individual development. Von Baer, about 1828, criticized this idea; but his own views on the subject were strongly coloured by the development hypothesis, and the subsequent history of the theory was largely influenced by what Von Baer taught, so much so that the recapitulation theory is often called his.

The study of the fossils was at that time just gaining scientific recognition; and Louis Agassiz, who had been a pupil of Cuvier, made the recapitulation theory, as we have already stated in Chapter VI, a very important factor in arranging the fossils found in the rocks. Agassiz specialized in the study of fossil fishes, but he extended his studies also to all other branches of animal life. He relied very largely upon the facts of embryology to make up the deficiencies in the fossils, and to prevent the confusion which he believed would result if these fossils were to be arranged wholly in accord with their anatomical differences alone. In 1857 he wrote, " I satisfied myself long ago that embryology furnishes the most trustworthy standard to determine the relative rank among animals." In the system ultimately worked out by him we find four great parallelisms or systems of relationships:

(1) Between the geological succession of animals and their taxonomic rank or structural position;
(2) Between the geological succession of animals and the embryonic development of their living representatives;
(3) Between the taxonomic or classification rank of animals and their embryonic development;
(4) All of these three series were again compared to the geographical distribution of animals. (P. E. Davidson, *The Recapitulation Theory,* p. 10; 1914.)

Agassiz became very enthusiastic over this method of comparison, for he thought he saw in these parallelisms the key to the history of creation. " The same series everywhere!" he exclaimed; and although he opposed Darwinism and organic evolution to the last, he never seemed to realize that, by means of his own artificial arrangement of the fossils so as to accord with both the embryonic development and the classification series of the living types, he was really inducing the scientific world to start chasing the phantom of organic evolution for the next two generations.

We have already seen that the early geological explorers, by a slip of logic, took their various local sequences of strata and magnified them into world sequences, thus giving us the modern fossiliferous onion-coat theory. It was a purely artificial act to arrange the various scattered deposits into a general scheme of world-development; but when Agassiz (and all subsequent workers in this field have followed him) arranged the details of this geological outline by comparison with the embryonic development of the living representatives, he was, if possible, *making it still more a purely artificial affair*. Henceforth the study of embryonic development was made the key, not only for classifying the fossils, but also for arranging the modern living animals in what was supposed to be their true relationship based on genetic affinity. Fritz Müller was one of the first to make an application of this method in the classification of the living animals; but it soon became the fashion to trace out genealogies, phylogenies, or racial histories according to this method. Ernst Haeckel was the most ardent in using this method; but for nearly a hundred years this method of comparison and of parallelisms has been regarded as the pole star in all biological and geological investigations.

When Darwin put forth the sixth edition of his *Origin of Species* in 1872, he made extensive use of the work of Fritz Müller, Haeckel and Agassiz, and urged the now familiar argument based on the interpretation of embryology, which says that the embryo repeats or recapitulates the history of its remote ancestors. He refers to Agassiz as believing that this is a universal law of nature; and he says, " We may hope hereafter to see the law proved true."

Haeckel was so much of a missionary for promulgating this doctrine that he seemed to stop at nothing if only he could proclaim this new scientific gospel. Nothing less than a complete classification of all living types and a tracing out of all the details of their developments from a single moneron, would satisfy him. Accordingly, in making his now notorious thirty stages in the development of man, he was compelled to manufacture several stages in order to have forms which would correspond to the gastrula, to the coelomula, etc., and these hypothetical forms, which were merely creatures of his own imagination, were given scientific names and deliberately inserted in his series, in order to show a complete evolution from the moneron to man which would be an exact parallel to the embryonic development of the modern individual from the ovum to maturity. In elaborating the details of this work he did not hesitate to " doctor " the embryos farther up the line and nearer to maturity, though his manipulations in this respect were denounced by many of his colleagues as little better than deliberate frauds. It will not be necessary for us here to enter into the details of this disagreeable subject. *The vicious logic*

*behind the whole scheme used by Haeckel was fully as
bad as any of those manufactured embryos which
have often been pointed out as his deliberate frauds.*

By the year 1866, Herbert Spencer criticized the
prevailing form of the recapitulation theory as it was
being taught by Haeckel. He declared that it is not
a fact that each higher organism passes through stages
in which it resembles the adult forms of lower organisms; and he also declared that " The embryological
parallelism is qualified by irregularities that are mostly
small, in many cases considerable, and occasionally
great."

In subsequent editions of his *Principles of Biology,*
Spencer omitted much of his criticisms of the recapitulation theory. As we have already shown in a previous chapter, Spencer was one of the strongest advocates of the theory of Lamarckism, or the theory of
the inheritance of acquired characters. The latter
theory seems to be intimately bound up with the recapitulation theory; indeed all of those leading scientists such as Darwin, Haeckel and Spencer, who have
lent their influence to the recapitulation theory, have
also been advocates of the doctrine of the inheritance
of acquired characters. Perhaps the waning popularity of the latter notion has helped to cast discredit
upon the former. However this may be, the two doctrines have gone the same road into comparative
oblivion. As we have dealt with the former doctrine
in a previous chapter, we are here concerned only with
the history of the recapitulation idea.

But it would never do to pass by the work of
Alpheus Hyatt, of Boston, who about the year 1866
made another important contribution to the theory by
an elaborate presentation of some of the facts of

geology which he thought were in harmony with this general doctrine. This phase of the subject has to do chiefly with the invertebrates, and is too technical to serve our purpose here. Suffice it to say that the school of paleontologists founded by Hyatt and Cope have become the strongest advocates of the recapitulation theory. However, like the work of Haeckel, the methods employed by Hyatt and his followers are artificial and quite illogical, in that they involve a vicious circle of reasoning which can really get us nowhere in any investigation of actual facts. Davidson, who admits far more foundation for this work of Hyatt and Cope than I would be willing to grant, shows that at best these comparisons based on the development of mollusks and other invertebrates must be of very limited application. He says, " It is plain that generalizations carried over from this rather circumscribed field of facts to the vertebrate or human territory, and more especially to the human nervous system or mind, can be the sheerest hypothetical possibilities." Indeed, the more detailed subsequent investigations among the mollusks, brachiopods and other invertebrates, have shown a constant series of examples which contradict every theory of recapitulation hitherto devised, even though this theory has been repeatedly amended and revised in order to correspond more nearly with these new discoveries.[1]

[1] Note.—For example, many of the echinoderms, which include the sea-urchins and the star-fishes, make very abrupt metamorphoses from the larval to the adult forms; and Mac-Bride argues that this cannot be a recapitulation, for " no species of animal could suddenly change its habits from swimming by means of cilia to walking with tube-feet." (*Camb. Nat. Hist.*, Vol. 1, p. 617.) In addition, the echinoderms start with " a marked bilateral symmetry " in

In a previous paragraph we have spoken of Darwin's sympathy for the belief of Agassiz and his expression of the hope that hereafter this " law " of Agassiz might be proved true. In commenting upon this remark, Adam Sedgwick, the eminent English embryologist, has said:

"But as Huxley has shown and as the whole course of paleontological investigation has demonstrated, no such statement can be made. The extinct forms of life are very similar to those now existing, and there is nothing specially embryonic about them. So that the facts, as we know them, lend no support to the theory." (*Darwin and Modern Science,* 1909, p. 174; quoted by Davidson, *op. cit.,* p. 29.)

Sedgwick's reference to Huxley is to some papers written by the latter in the years 1855 and 1862. In the latter paper Huxley wrote: "An impartial survey of positively ascertained truth then negatives the common doctrines of progressive modification, or a necessary progress from more or less embryonic forms . . . it either shows us no evidence of any such modification or demonstrates it to have been very slight."

And all this, it must be remembered, is in spite of the fact that the paleontologists have had the world to pick from, and have been able to arrange the various geological formations in almost any way to suit their fancy, or to suit what they thought *ought* to be the proper serial arrangement of these fossil groups.

Zittel, the great German geologist, writing in 1895 regarding the relationship of paleontology and the re-

the larval stage, and their subsequent change to radial symmetry "constitutes one of the most remarkable life-histories known in the animal kingdom" (*Id.,* p. 429). The recapitulation theory sounds like nonsense when confronted with facts like these.

capitulation theory, said that the embryonic development of living organisms could " afford but an unsafe basis for the reconstruction of ancient faunas and floras, since experience teaches that the biogenetic law [the recapitulation theory] is frequently veiled or completely obscured owing to various causes." After giving a number of illustrations of the absurdities involved in applying this recapitulation theory to the fossil forms, he remarks that these examples " may suffice to show how trivial are the discoveries concerning existence in earlier periods of earth-history that can follow from ontogenetic [embryonic] researches alone."

V

If we come now to a consideration of the present status of the recapitulation theory, we shall find that it has very few defenders among the biologists of first-rate importance. Adam Sedgwick will admit that there is a general correspondence between the developing embryo and the evolutionary history of the race, for he is still a believer in the general doctrine of organic evolution. But Sedgwick can see only an agreement between the two series in their broad outlines. " The generalization," he says, " undoubtedly had its origin in the fact that there is what may be called a family resemblance between embryos and larvae, but this resemblance, which is by no means exact, is largely superficial and does not extend to anatomical detail."

In his work dealing with the recapitulation theory, a work to which I have been largely indebted, Davidson gives us the following summary of the present situation:

" From these authoritative statements it appears that the facts of embryonic resemblances fail to support recapitulation in all three of its main implications. The order of appearance of characters is not uniformly, or even commonly, that required by recapitulation, which is first those representative of the order, and then in succession, of the family, genus, species. In the second place, embryonic resemblance in comparable stages does not vary directly with remoteness of kinship, but shows often very great divergence from this rule, indicating unlike careers in lines of descent in the same group and therefore great diversity in the appearance of variation during development, at any period, and not only at the adolescent or adult end of ontogeny. Finally, where resemblance does exist, it is not identity, nor even close [resemblance], implying that the effect of variation upon the same ancestral structure has not been the same in allied lines of descent, but has been productive of new structures, suggesting perhaps in broad outlines the ancestral structure, but still variant in every case, and essentially so " (pp. 34, 35).

Depéret, the French paleontologist, refers to Haeckel's hypothetical ancestors of man as " visions of the mind," because no objective fossil evidence can be pointed to as corresponding to them. Geoffrey Smith has given quite similar criticisms of the attempts to build up a complete account of the animal kingdom from its alleged primitive forms. He says that we can get along very well in arranging the various animals in their appropriate phyla, and give some appearance of relationship between the genera and families in these phyla. " But when we attempt to go behind the phyla and discover their origin and interrelationships, we leave the firm ground altogether and wander in a slippery and nebulous region of speculation.

" It is true," he goes on, " that certain hypotheses of a plausible character have been suggested which have satisfied uncritical minds, and which we often hear advanced as a part of ascertained science and accepted in an otiose spirit.

. . . But what is there of reality in these speculations? They rest not on any objective evidence but upon the tendency of the mind to pass from the apparently simple to the manifestly complex, and to regard the former as primitive and ancestral, and the latter as secondary and derivative." (*Primitive Animals,* pp. 14, *et seq.*)

In his article on embryology in the latest edition of the *Encyclopædia Britannica,* Professor Sedgwick enumerates a series of structures in the embryo of the higher vertebrates which are similar in a general way to some structures in the lower orders of animals. For instance, the heart is at first a simple tubular structure, corresponding in a general way to the simple heart of the lower orders; and only in the later stages do we have a heart of four chambers. The skeleton, which is bony in the adult, passes through a stage entirely without bone and consisting mainly of cartilage. Plenty of instances of this sort might be mentioned, for the works on comparative embryology are full of them. *But they are only the inevitable consequences of the development of the individual from the simple to the complex.* The final structures could not be produced without going through the preparatory stages just enumerated any more than one would expect to build a house without first putting in the foundation, subsequently putting up walls, and finally putting on the roof. No sensible person would think for a moment that a builder could reverse this process and begin with the roof and finally put in the foundation. A large number of the structures in the developing embryo which seem to be parallel to the structures found in the lower orders, are of this character. But side by side with these facts exist other facts or other embryonic conditions for which no place can be found in the theory of recapitulation. I quote again from Sedgwick:

"Examples of embryonic characters which are not found in the adults of other vertebrates are the following: At a certain stage of development the central nervous system has the form of a groove in the skin; there is a communication at the hind end of the body between the neural and alimentary canals; the mouth aperture at the first has the form of an elongated slit; the growing end of the Wolffian duct is in some groups continuous with the ectoderm; and the retina is at one stage a portion of the wall of the medullary canal. In the embryos of the lower vertebrates many other instances of the same interesting character might be mentioned." (*Encyc. Brit.*, Vol. IX, p. 322.)

I think we shall agree with Miall, in his address before the British Association, in 1897, where he says: "The best facts of the recapitulationist are striking and valuable, but they are much rarer than the thoroughgoing recapitulationist admits; he has picked out all the big strawberries and put them at the top of the basket" (*Proceedings*, 1897; p. 682).

William His, who may almost be called the father of human embryology, has given us some of the most sensible remarks concerning this matter of embryonic development:

"In the entire series of forms which a developing organism runs through, each form is the necessary antecedent step of the following. If the embryo is to reach the complicated end-forms, it must pass, step by step, through the simpler ones. Each step of the series is the physiological consequence of the preceding stage and the necessary condition of the following. Jumps, or short cuts of the development process, are unknown in the physiological process of development. If embryonic forms are the inevitable precedents of the mature forms, because the more complicated forms must pass through the simpler, we can understand the fact that paleontological forms are so often like the embyronic forms of to-day. The paleontological forms are embryonal, because they have remained at the lower stage of development, and the present embryos must pass also through lower stages in order to reach the higher. But it is by no means necessary for the later, higher forms to pass through embryonal forms because their ancestors have once existed in this condition" (quoted by Morgan, *Evolution and Adaptation,* p. 71).

Accordingly, Professor His labels Haeckel's biogenetic " law " as " a mere by-path," and says that it is " not necessary at all for the explanation of the facts of embryology."

Oscar Hertwig also says: " We must drop the expression ' repetition of the form of extinct forefathers,' and put in its place the repetition of forms which are necessary for organic development, and lead from the simple to the complex." This is sensible and scientifically accurate.

P. C. Mitchell, in his article on " Evolution " in the *Encyclopædia Britannica,* speaks of the change which has come about in scientific opinion regarding this matter of recapitulation. He says:

" The most striking general change has been against seeing in the facts of ontogeny [embryonic development] any direct evidence as to phylogeny [ancestral history]. The general proposition as to a parallelism between individual and ancestral development is no doubt indisputable; but extended knowledge of the very different ontogenetic histories of closely allied forms has led us to a much fuller conception of the mode in which stages in embroynic and larval history have been modified in relation to their surroundings, and to a consequent reluctance to attach detailed importance to the embryological argument for evolution." (Vol. X, p. 35.)

The list of quotations which might be given to show that conservative scientists have given up any dependence upon the recapitulation theory, would be a long one. One more of this character will suffice.

" The critical comments of such embryologists as O. Hertwig, Keibel, and Vialleton, indeed, have practically torn to shreds the aforesaid fundamental biogenetic law. Its almost unanimous abandonment has left considerably at a loss those investigators who sought in the structure of organisms the key to their remote origin or to their relationships." (*Sci. Amer. Mo., Feb.,* 1921, p. 121.)

It is an indication of the reactionary tendencies of the modern propagandists of the evolution doctrine, to find Vernon Kellogg saying that this recapitulation theory " is one of the strongest of the evidences of evolution " (*Evolution the Way of Man*, p. 54; 1924).

VI

A brief series of illustrations drawn from modern industrial life, will serve to make several points in this discussion more clear.

The wheelbarrow may be spoken of as the most " primitive " of vehicles. Of course, there is no historical evidence to show that it was really the first form of vehicle, any more than there is evidence to show that the monorail form of railway was the first of its kind. But the wheelbarrow is the simplest of the vehicles, in point of structure, and its chief characteristic is that it has but one wheel. The bicycle is next higher in the scale, the two-wheeled cart being of the same grade or stage of development, though quite independent in its " evolution " from the one-wheeled form. The four-wheeled buggy may be placed next in the scale, though various forms of tricycle indicate divergent forms which ceased to progress any further. The buggy, however, grades up into the automobile, and then into the six-wheeled locomotive, from that into the eight-wheeled, and lastly into the sixteen-wheeled type. The latter may be regarded as having evolved from the one-wheeled type, the changes shown in the size and character of its wheels and other parts being exactly what one would naturally expect, in view of its greatly changed environment and habits. Indeed, in each case mentioned above, we see a very remarkable adaptation in all the parts of the machine to the uses for which it is employed.

But now, if we look into the methods of manufacture of any of these machines, we shall find that they closely parallel each other in their building, just as the various kinds of animals parallel each other in their embryonic development. And the reason is the same in each of these two groups of cases, namely, *efficiency*. These various kinds of machines are built (when manufactured on a large scale) in the most efficient and the most economical way; and similarly we must suppose that the embryos of the horse, the chick, the guinea pig, or man are each built in the best and most efficient manner possible, considering the final form, or the end-product. The few cases where the process seems to be of a round-about or circuitous character and not as direct as we might wish, are doubtless the most direct and efficient method, if we could understand all the facts. To think otherwise would be to assume a knowledge and a wisdom superior to that displayed by " nature," or really by the God behind nature.

If we were to go the rounds of the factories where the various kinds of automobiles are manufactured, we should find much the same methods employed in them all. At a certain stage in their development, one cannot clearly distinguish between a Ford or a Rolls-Royce or a Cadillac, this resemblance being carried out in hundreds of details in the development of the various parts. All this is exactly parallel to the many ways in which the developing embryo of man resembles that of the horse or the elephant; and is for the very same reason, namely, *efficiency*. The men who are building automobiles, no matter what the make, are each trying to build them in the most direct and most efficient manner which they can devise, considering the end-products which they have in mind. And in the earlier stages of the growth of these machines the Ford resembles other cars much more closely than it does in its completed form, just as the first stages of the human embryo resemble the corresponding stages of the dog or the horse more closely than do the mature forms.

VII

This is about all there really is to the long notorious argument for evolution based on the recapitulation theory. This theory started when the facts of embryology were very imperfectly known; it was developed and promoted on an artificial arrangement of the fossils which was alleged to harmonize with the embryonic development of the modern individual. It has now collapsed with the exposure of the artificiality of this geological arrangement of the fossils, and with a more accurate and complete knowledge of the embryonic development, which shows that the latter does not correspond with the geological series even when the fossils have been arranged artificially to show as much resemblance as possible. In short, the recapitulation theory as an argument for organic evolution was founded on ignorance and deceptive comparisons; it has now outlived its popularity among those evolutionists who feel obliged to depend henceforth upon honest arguments to promote their theory. To continue to use the recapitulation argument as it was used by Haeckel and Darwin, can no longer be regarded as an indication of intellectual honesty.

BIBLIOGRAPHY

Agar, W. E., *Cytology;* 1920.

Davidson, Percy E., *The Recapitulation Theory;* 1914.

McEwen, R. S., *A Textbook of Vertebrate Embryology;* 1923.

Sedgwick, Adam, *Embryology,* in *Encycl. Brit.;* Vol. IX, pp. 314-329.

Weismann A., *The Germ Plasm;* English Translation; 1893.

Wilson, E. B., *The Cell;* 1900.

VIII

THE BLOODY LADDER

I

DURING the period when pure Darwinism had its vogue, which may be defined as the latter decades of the nineteenth century and the first decade of the twentieth, Darwin's doctrine of natural selection or survival of the fittest seemed to have accomplished two very definite things. It seemed to have destroyed completely the many evidences of design in nature which had formerly been pointed to by theologians and students of philosophy as proofs of purposive planning on the part of the God of nature. It not only destroyed these supposed evidences of design; but it substituted for the design argument an explanation of the adaptations in nature which was so heartless, so full of all those qualities which we regard as wicked and detestable, that to attribute such a method of creating the world to an intelligent Creator necessarily changed completely the character of such a Creator. Darwinian evolution never properly proved that materialism is true; that is, it never properly proved that God *could not* have made the world by the process of organic evolution. Quite evidently a creative Intelligence *could* make the world by such a process; but to believe in such a process would necessarily change completely our ideas of the *kind* of Creator behind nature. To say nothing of the record in the Bible, it is impossible for a rational mind to believe that an all-wise, all-powerful, God of supreme kindliness and love would ever have produced the world by such a cruel, heartless process; least of all that He could have produced man, the crowning triumph of this work, by such a long-drawn out ordeal of cruelty, torture and villainy.

Thus, in addition to the strictly scientific arguments which will be presented in the following pages against the theory of natural selection, we must here for a little while consider some rational and moral objections to this theory. And surely it is a very narrow view of the universe which would forbid our bringing in these studies here as a part of our general argument. There are many things in the realm of morals and philosophy which are just as sure and just as easily understood as anything that we can derive from biology or geology. And it is perfectly proper that we should allow these considerations a large place in our full consideration of these problems. The stench arising from a putrid carcass will inform us of decomposition, without any elaborate knowledge of organic chemistry; and the beauty of a sunset can be appreciated without any profound knowledge of optics or of meteorology. In the same way our intuitive knowledge of justice, and truth, and benevolence may serve as safer guides in attempting to read the mysterious messages of nature, than will our conclusions based on such studies as those presented by Malthus, *On Population,* or those made so popular in the *Origin of Species.*

II

The merest tyro in the study of organic evolution can see that the doctrine of survival of the fittest, or

natural selection, makes some of the most morally objectionable characteristics manifested by animals and
men the ladder by which all true progress has been
attained. In other words, those qualities among the
lower races of men, or among the animals, which we
rightly regard as objectionable and blameworthy, such
as selfishness, vindictiveness, and a heartless disregard
of the feelings and desires of others, have been made
by Darwin and his followers the chief factor in their
scheme of organic evolution. And although pure Darwinism is not now as popular as it once was as a
method of explaining the causes of evolution, yet it
still holds such a large place in any scheme of evolution that it may rightly be considered here in this connection, and may well be subjected to all the scrutiny
and the critical analysis which we can bring to bear
upon it.

Huxley illustrates this point for us, when he says:

"For his successful progress as far as the savage state,
man has been largely indebted to those qualities which he
shares with the ape and the tiger."

John Fiske is equally candid in saying that, according to the theory of natural selection, nature has put
a high premium on these cruel and heartless characteristics, by making them the bloody ladder by which
the race has ascended to its present condition. For
he says:

"Those most successful primitive men from whom civilized peoples are descended must have excelled in treachery
and cruelty, as in quickness of wit and strength of will."

On another occasion Fiske has given us a more general statement of the problem which we are here considering:

"Theology has much to say about original sin. This original sin is neither more nor less than the brute-inheritance which every man carries with him."

Another statement from this same point of view, this time from J. Arthur Thomson, will help us to see the true inwardness of this doctrine of the struggle for existence:

"Tone it down as you will, the fact remains that Darwinism regards animals as going upstairs, in a struggle for individual ends, often on the corpses of their fellows, often by a blood-and-iron competition, often by a strange mixture of blood and cunning, in which each looks out for himself and extinction besets the hindmost."

A. R. Wallace, who gives us this quotation in his *World of Life,* expresses the hope that Thomson has somewhat toned down this harsh view of the struggle for existence. But we should remember that Huxley spoke even more emphatically regarding the essential cruelty of nature and all the biological processes by which evolution in his view has been accomplished. And the point which we shall endeavour to make in this connection is that this view of the fundamental processes of nature *is a real libel on God,* the author of nature, who, if He were a God of love and also all-powerful and all-wise, could never be supposed to have brought about the development of organic forms in any such hideously cruel fashion. In addition to this moral indictment, we shall see that there are very grave scientific objections to the theory, so grave, in fact, that most modern scientists have long since repudiated

natural selection as in any material way having contributed to the development of organic forms.

I am not here concerned with the larger or primary
problem of the origin of evil, that is, with the origin
of the physical and moral evil in the universe. This
problem has been touched upon by the present writer
elsewhere; though the subject is not by any means a
new one for Christian philosophy. In passing, it may
be noted here that most evolutionists hold matter to
be eternal, and to have an inherent quality of unman-
ageableness about it which God Himself is not competent to deal with. This doctrine of a finite God, as
it is usually called, struggling to do the best He can
under the circumstances, has been represented by such
men as William James, J. S. Mill, F. C. S. Schiller,
Henri Bergson, and others. We need not pause here
to consider how utterly contrary to Christianity such
a system really is. We are here concerned with the
moral and religious implications of natural selection as
the method of accounting for the origin and development of all the forms of animal and plant life.

F. W. Nietzsche (1844-1900), the notorious philosopher of the *Superman*, was one of the most outspoken
in his bald glorification of the bloody ladder of natural
selection as the only means of progress. Not only did
he glorify war as the chief means by which individuals
and states progress to higher stages of existence; he
also tried to throw a halo of glory around those qualities of mind and character which for two thousand
years have been considered the very antithesis of
Christianity. Nietzsche was unsparing in his scorn of
all those characteristics of mind and character which
were taught to the world by the lowly Nazarene.

Many statements, like the following, could be culled from his writings:

" Such ideas as mercy, and pity, and charity are pernicious, for they mean a transference of power from the strong to the weak, whose proper business it is to serve the strong. Remember that self-sacrifice and brotherliness and love are not real moral instincts at all, but merely manufactured compunctions to keep you from being your true self. Remember that man is essentially selfish."

Elsewhere he tells us that " Egoism is the prime characteristic of the noble soul;" and in his famous genealogy of morals he divides mankind into just two classes,—masters and slaves; he has one kind of morality for the one, and a very different system of " slave morality " for the others; and the only use which he has for the slave caste is to serve as useful tools for the masters in their unconditioned will to power.

Again, he says:

" Here is the new law, O my brethren, which I promulgate unto you! Become hard; for creative spirits are hard. And you must find a supreme blessedness in imposing the mark of your hand, in inscribing your will, upon thousands and thousands, as on soft wax."

We must admit that Nietzsche was at least bold and consistent in applying the ethics of Darwinism all the way up the line, even to the ethical life of man in both his private and his international relations. Huxley, however, was not willing to follow the doctrine of natural selection thus to the end of the road. He balked when he was confronted with applying the doctrine of the struggle for existence to man in his social and national relations. He taught that by the formation of communities or nations a new order of things came into existence, the laws and ethics of which are wholly different from those of the " cosmic order," which is the term used to designate the order of things prevailing under the long upward climb of mankind through the struggle for existence. In other words, in order for men to live together in anything like peace and quietness, co-operation and altruism must be the rules of the social order; and such a code of ethics is obviously exactly contrary to the code hitherto prevailing, according to Darwinian evolution. Neither Huxley nor any of his followers have shown *why* this ethical somersault, this complete reversal of the ethics of the " cosmic order," should have taken place. Indeed, it is hard to understand why a code of ethics which evolved a subman from an ape, and further developed this subman into a Menes, or a Hammurabi, or a Julius Caesar, should not be expected in our day to develop a race of supermen, *a la* Nietzsche. No doubt Huxley had learned by experience that it was more agreeable if others around him practiced altruism and the Christian virtues rather than the selfish code of a constant struggle for supremacy and for survival even at the expense of others. And so he introduced his reversal of all those principles by which mankind had lifted itself above the plane of the beasts of the field.

There was no flaw in the logic by which the Prussian militarists appealed to Darwinian biology as the sanction for their international ruffianism, in seeking to live up to their motto: *"Deutschland über alles."* But he has only an infantile sense of logic who would attempt to equate either of these systems with the sublime ethics which has been taught us by the Prophet of Galilee. If the latter has come to us from the God of the universe, the former is a libel on the methods by which this same God created the plants and animals of our world and now sustains their existence.

III

George Paulin has attacked the theory from another angle in a book, entitled *No Struggle for Existence, No Natural Selection* (T. & T. Clark, Edinburgh; 1908). He rightly charges that Darwin's theory was an attack against the concept of a benevolent Creator and a designing Intelligence. But his chief charge is against the picture of a pitiless struggle throughout the organic world, which he claims is not true. Darwin had claimed that we do not know in any single instance just what checks are used by Nature to keep a certain kind of animal from multiplying unduly and over-running the earth; and he assumed that it was by the limits of the food supply, and by the competition, fierce and perpetual, for food and for the opportunity to pro-create, that the numbers were kept down. Darwin and his followers had always represented nature as " careful of the type," but absolutely " careless of the single life." In other words, Darwinism had always represented nature as wholly indifferent to the happiness of the individual animal (or even the individual man), and as contemplating only the slow, long-drawn out evolutionary process, the individuals being constantly sacrificed on the mirage of an alleged " far-off divine event " toward which the whole creation was supposed to be moving by an ever tantalizing asymptote, while present misery is always the lot of everything that lives.

All this, says Paulin, is wrong, and a heartless libel

on the God of nature. He shows that starvation does not act as the check upon any type of life, but that various other checks, in the way of instincts, have been provided, by which the numbers of any particular species of animal, whether carnivorous or herbivorous, are kept within bounds and about at a constant number from year to year and from century to century. Even such animals as the lion and the tiger do not perish from mutual slaughter or from starvation; their numbers are kept constant and within bounds by other checks which involve no such wide-spread suffering. The precautionary checks are different for the different kinds of animals; but in all cases the balanced economy of nature is maintained without any such fierce struggle for existence as Darwin had pictured as the universal lot of all organic life. Death is the common lot of all living things, in this world of sin; but the death that comes to the vast majority of animals is quick and almost without suffering. And the revolting picture of nature which we get from Malthus and Darwin is not true.

IV

Still further, it is quite unreasonable to suppose that a relentless struggle for air and sunlight among plants, or for food and various other opportunities among animals, could tend toward a higher or more elevated type, as a general result. There is hardship and suffering; there is a modicum of competition both among plants and among animals. But such conditions never tend toward greater symmetry or larger size, nor do they ever tend toward the elevation of the type subject to these conditions. *On the contrary, hardship, privation, and the struggle for existence must always tend toward degeneracy and degradation.* Such conditions might be supposed to have produced the sneaking, cowardly coyote out of the wolf, the Indian elephant (*Elephas indicus*) out of the much larger mammoth (*E. primigenius*) or imperial elephant (*E. imperator*), or the modern hippopotamus (*H. amphibius*) out of the Pleistocene form (*H. major*), just as the dwarfed, scrub pines and other trees near the timber line have been produced by their hard environment out of the kinds found lower down the mountain side. In short, hardship and unsuitable environment do not develop, they degrade in every single instance; and any philosophy of organic life which reverses this universal law of nature, and tries to evolve the higher and more beautiful and more complex by means of hardship and an unsuitable environment, must be false.

V

In his ostentatiously candid manner Darwin admitted that, " If it could be demonstrated that any complex organ existed, which could not possibly have been formed by numerous, successive, slight modifications, my theory would absolutely break down " (*Origin*, 5th ed., 1869, p. 227). Two men were prominent in taking him at his word while he was yet alive, St. George Mivart and Herbert Spencer; while since those latter decades of the nineteenth century a great chorus of voices has arisen against the theory of natural selection, until, just before he died, John Burroughs declared that Darwin had been " shorn of his selection theories as completely as Samson was shorn of his locks " (*Atlantic Monthly*, August, 1920; p. 237).

Mivart especially emphasized two points, first that

" natural selection utterly fails to account for the conservation and development of the minute and rudimentary beginnings, the slight and infinitesimal commencements of structures, however useful those structures may afterwards become " (*The Genesis of Species*, p. 35). This failure of the theory to account for the beginnings of organs and structures has since been dwelt upon by many scientists, de Vries ending his best known work with the words, quoted from another, that the theory might " explain the survival of the fittest, but it could never explain the arrival of the fittest." The other argument made by Mivart had to do with the many similar organs and structures which must have been developed quite independently of each other. Mivart, indeed, did not consider this latter point as telling against the general theory of organic evolution, only against Darwin's special theory of natural selection; but in Chapter VI of the present work, I have extended the argument so as to include the whole theory.

Spencer's objections chiefly consisted in the enumeration of structures the origin of which it seems evident cannot be explained by natural selection. Among other examples, he dwelt upon the impossibility of accounting for the origin and development of *co-ordinated sets* of structures, declaring that it was incredible that these related or interdependent parts should vary simultaneously in the same required manner, as a mere matter of chance, as postulated by Darwin's selection theories. Spencer was not arguing against the general theory of organic evolution, but against natural selection and in favour of the inheritance of acquired characters as the only adequate explanation. And he summed up the case in the oft-quoted words:

" Close contemplation of the facts impresses me more strongly than ever with the two alternatives—either there has been inheritance of acquired characters, or there has been no evolution " (*The Inadequacy of Natural Selection,* p. 20). In Germany, Haeckel took practically the same position, while in America, E. D. Cope and others likewise contended strongly for the Lamarckian " factor," as it came to be called; and this group among biologists has since been known as the Neo-Lamarckian school.

But August Weismann in Germany, and Wallace and Lankester in England, took up the cause of natural selection with great zeal. The former was the propounder of the theory of the continuity of the germplasm, in the light of which theory (based on an almost iron-clad argument derived from the behaviour of the germ-cells) it appeared impossible for any of the effects of the environment to change the germplasm, which according to this view of the case passes along in an essentially immortal stream from genera tion to generation, quite unaffected by any influences which may be brought to bear upon the body. According to Weismann and these Neo-Darwinians, inheritance does not take place from the body of the parent to that of the child; but the child inherits from the parent germ-cell, the body of the parent being merely the carrier, the nurse, as it were, of these self-perpetuating germ-cells, which are thus held in trust for the coming generations, as Wilson expresses it.

The followers of Weismann out-Darwined Darwin in their stand for natural selection as the sole and only sufficient cause of organic evolution; and they scornfully demanded one single well-authenticated example of the inheritance of acquired characters which would stand close investigation. J. Arthur Thomson devotes nearly a hundred pages of his treatise on *Heredity* to the discussion of this phase of the question, and concludes that there is no reliable scientific evidence in favour of the inheritance of acquired characters. He says, in summary of his argument:

> " The question resolves itself into a matter of fact: Have we any concrete evidence to warrant us believing that definite modifications are ever, as such or in any representative degree, transmitted? It appears to us that we have not. But to say dogmatically that such transmission is impossible, is unscientific. In regard to that, the truly scientific position is one of active skepticism (*thätige Skepsis*)" (p. 242).

In other words, these Neo-Darwinians are from Missouri; they want to be shown some well-authenticated examples. And in spite of all the noisy claims of Kammerer, Redfield, and others, they remain still very much unconvinced. Indeed, their skepticism has become so active that they can listen to alleged examples only with considerable signs of impatience. Well trained physicists and even intelligent mechanics have developed the same " active skepticism " toward the subject of perpetual motion; and for the same reasons.

Accordingly, we have here exhibited what some people not sympathetic with natural science have called the modern scientific civil war. On the one side, Paul Kammerer of Vienna, and Prof. E. W. MacBride of England, with a small but determined following, have pledged themselves to the theory of the inheritance of acquired characters; and they ask their opponents how natural selection is going to start a single organ of a single organic type; they then follow this question up with the taunt that, if it cannot *start* anything, what is the use of invoking its supposed ability to improve the structures after they have all been built? On the other hand, such men as Sir E. Ray Lankester, J. Arthur Thomson, Edwin Grant Conklin, and Henry Fairfield Osborn retort that they are willing to believe in the " Lamarckian factor " of acquired characters whenever any good, clear, unambiguous examples are produced; but until that time they will continue to depend upon natural selection as the chief, if not the only, factor in organic evolution.

VI

However, it is in reality a three-angled fight, another variation of the eternal triangle. For the Mendelians are also in the ring; indeed they seem to be carrying off almost all the honours. They stand for the origin of species by " jumps " or mutations; and they are very enthusiastic in bringing forward and explaining their specimens which they have manufactured, so to speak, to prove their contentions. They would like to believe in the inheritance of acquired characters, if they could only see any way whereby the effects of the environment or of use and disuse could become registered in the chromosomes, and thus be passed along the stream of the germ-plasm in heredity. But as well authenticated examples are still lacking, they fall back upon some unknown method by which the chromosomes may become modified, and thus these modifications get within the charmed circle of the germ-plasm and become a part of the future inheritance. But some Mendelians have little or no use for the theory of natural selection. In their estimation, this theory was founded on many mistaken ideas, and is now of little scientific interest, except historically,—Darwin's theory helped to make the general theory of organic evolution "a going concern," as J. Arthur Thomson expresses it. They respect it for the good it has done.

The present attitude toward Darwinism among most biologists in America is well represented by the writings of Thomas Hunt Morgan, of Columbia. In England, William Bateson is one of the leaders of the Mendelians; but there are many others scarcely second to him both in England and on the Continent. In fact the Mendelians are so nearly masters of the entire field that the voices raised in revolt against them are weak and timorous; though once in a while someone like E. W. MacBride is heard shouting that Mendelism has led the evolutionary hosts into a *cul-de-sac* (*Science Progress,* January, 1922).

An admirable statement of the modern biological attitude is given by Robert Heath Lock, in his *Variation, Heredity, and Evolution,* London, 1920; the third chapter of which deals specifically with natural selection. He adduces many strong arguments against the validity of this theory; but the following may be taken as a summary of his attitude:

"No one questions the validity of natural selection as a means of exterminating types which are unfitted for their environment—there is clearly a tendency for the fittest types to survive, once they have come into existence. Nor can there be any doubt that species in general are well adapted to the conditions which their environments present. But when this is admitted, it does not necessarily follow that natural selection, directing the accumulation of minute differences, has been the method by which these adapted forms have originated" (p. 61).

Dr. J. C. Willis, in the sixth chapter of his recent volume, *Age and Area* (1922), has presented with much force several of the well-known objections to the theory of natural selection. Various other modern works might be mentioned which have effectually disposed of natural selection as being in any sense a *vera causa* of organic development. Indeed, it may be truthfully said that any one who in this year 1924 still stands up for natural selection as an explanation of organic evolution, is too hopelessly behind the times to be reached with any further arguments of mine. However, it will not be amiss to present two or three more very recent statements.

A. G. Tansley, at the Liverpool meeting of the British Association in 1923, declared: " In regard to a multitude of characters, there is not only no proof, but not the slightest reason to suppose that they have now, or ever did have, any survival value at all."

At the Cincinnati meeting of the American Association, December, 1923, J. Playfair McMurrich, the retiring President, said regarding natural selection:

" The biological world of to-day does not ascribe to that factor the importance that Darwin gave it. Its action cannot be denied, it is self-evident to any observer of Nature's ways who finds ' that of fifty seeds she often brings but one to bear.' It plays an important rôle in the suppression of the unfit rather than in the survival of the fittest, but it can act only on variations sufficiently pronounced to determine life or death. It has been shown in several cases that what seem trivial variations may, under certain conditions, lead to fatal results; but even admitting these, it is difficult to believe that many of the minute differences that distinguish species have selective value." (*Science*, Jan. 25, 1924; *Supplement.*)

Here is another declaration from a very high English authority:

" Natural selection is a theory of the origin of adaptations, and in my judgment there is ample evidence that specific differences are not as a rule differences of adaptation. Therefore natural selection does not explain specific differences. It is recognized now that in the cultivation of animals and plants the marked and constant characters which distinguish races are not, as Darwin believed, the gradual result of continued selection, but are mutations which have arisen spontaneously in definite form, not by successive stages. Does any one believe now that the rose comb in fowls is the result of a series of stages due to artificial selection?" (J. T. Cunningham, *Nature,* March 3, 1923.)

This author makes reference to a book of his own, as a justification of his opinion and as showing why he considers " the theory of natural selection to be obsolete." He goes on to say that this " conclusion, of course, is not disproved by the fact that many naturalists still believe in the theory in America, and elsewhere. But there are specialists in evolution, as well as in systematic zoology and in other branches; and I venture to say that few who have made a special and practical study of evolution, and are well acquainted with recent progress in that study, have much faith in natural selection." (*Ib., id.*)

VII

We may safely conclude from all this that a great idol has tumbled down, an idol which while it stood on its feet was clamorously praised and worshipped by more atheists and more enemies of the Bible than ever bowed before the ancient Baal or Apollo. Even in its ruined state we see belated reverence still addressed to the place in biology where it once stood; and belated hymns are still being chanted for it by such people as the Marxian Socialists and the teachers in the grammar schools and the high schools of America. The psychologists are still using miniatures of it in the classroom, while the " progressive " theologians still keep on parroting the eulogies in its praise which they learned from the hod-carriers of natural science, when the latter were first constructing its shrine a half-century ago.

But for the scholars of the world, the ones who persist in thinking for themselves and who form their conclusions only on facts and still more facts, the niche is vacant where once stood that golden " Anti-Genesis," as Haeckel used to call it.   And while some are sorrowfully groping around for something to put in the vacant place, the more reverent are directing their eyes upward to that inscription in the heavens, " In the beginning God created the heaven and the earth."

BIBLIOGRAPHY

Bishop, R. B., *Evolution Criticised;* 1918.

Conklin, E. G., *Heredity and Environment;* 1921.

Dennert, E., *At the Deathbed of Darwinism;* English Translation; 1904.

Fairhurst, A., *Organic Evolution Considered;* 1913.

Lock, R. H., *Variation, Heredity, and Evolution;* 1920.

Mivart, St. G., *The Genesis of Species;* 1871.

Morgan, T. H., *A Critique of the Theory of Evolution;* 1916.

Paulin, George, *No Struggle for Existence;* 1908.

Spencer, Herbert, *The Inadequacy of Natural Selection;* 1893.

Thomson, J. A., *Heredity;* 1919.

Wallace, A. R., *Darwinism;* 1889.

     The World of Life; 1911.

Willey, Arthur, *Convergence in Evolution;* 1911.

Willis, J. C. (and others), *Age and Area;* 1922.

IX

UBINAM GENTIUM SUMUS?

I

WE have reached the conclusion of our argument. But in summing up the verdict which we are to bring in, it may be well to look briefly at the theory of evolution in its broader aspects, what is termed cosmic evolution, a theory which designs to explain the development of stellar mist or planetesimals into organic life and the mind of a Newton or a Kelvin. For cosmic evolution undertakes to explain with its formula everything from the nebula to the Sermon on the Mount and the struggle for the League of Nations.

But natural science must not be held responsible for any such mechanistic philosophy as that. Indeed, on every point where science can come to grips with such a philosophy, the verdict of cold fact and reason is overwhelmingly against it. For example, let us take the nebular hypothesis of Kant and La Place. " Probably no philosophic conception has ever received such universal acceptance by the modern world as the Laplacian theory. Yet it is not true. It has been conclusively shown by Professors Chamberlin and Moulton that the theory breaks down at every point where attacked by present-day physics and kinetics. The conception of an originally molten globe must also be discarded." (H. L. Fairchild, *Scientific Monthly,* July, 1924; p. 95.)

And the verdict of strict science must be that none of the substitute theories of the origin of the solar system are any better. Certain general facts, however, seem to be in process of determination. Astronomers seem agreed that the entire universe is definitely limited in extent, and that it consists of some 1,500 million suns, with a total diameter of about three hundred thousand light-years. Of course some will have it that a serial order can be arranged for the stars, this serial order being supposed to represent the various stages of their development. But all are now agreed that whatever explanation we adopt for the origin of the solar system must be in accord with the behaviour of all the stars scattered throughout the universe. In other words, the explanation which we adopt for the origin of our solar system must be in accord with universal cosmic laws.

Yet J. H. Jeans, in a recent address before the Royal Institution, London, tells us that astronomy knows absolutely nothing of any other system of worlds throughout the whole universe which resembles our solar system in even the slightest degree. He says: " Not a single system is known outside our solar system which resembles it in the least degree " (*Nature*, March 1, 1924; p. 337). Jeans goes on to explain the bearings of the so-called tidal theory upon this problem of the origin of our solar system; and he shows that *if we can assume several arbitrary and peculiar conditions* we can explain the probable formation of the sun and its accompanying system of planets with their satellites. But he admits that this theory is not to be taken too seriously, and that it is " far too early to claim that it can fully explain the origin of our system." He concludes by saying that the claim to consideration which this tidal theory presents " is rather that, so far as I know, it provides the only theory of that origin which is not open to obvious and insuperable objections " (p. 340).

But Harlow Shapley denies that we can recognize any signs of stellar evolution among the stars, and there is no higher authority in the world on this particular phase of astronomy.

"In still another way can we make valuable use of the long base-line provided by the remote clusters. A considerable analysis of the distribution of spectral types among the giant stars shows no measurable difference for near and distant globular clusters. This strongly suggests, of course, that the nearest systems are not appreciably more advanced in their evolution; but because of the finite velocity of light and the great differences in distance, they are, in our records, nearly 200,000 years older than the farthest ones. With these globular clusters we can, in effect, examine the process of stellar evolution throughout an interval of 2,000 centuries. We find no evidence of change in that interval of time." (Harlow Shapley, in an address before the British Astronomical Association, on May 31, 1922; *Nature,* October 21 and 28, 1922.)

This is a splendid testimony, and it ought to silence all those noisy near-scientists who keep telling us that astronomy shows us many other universes in actual process of stellar evolution.

We may dismiss all speculations regarding the origin of our solar system, because, to use the expressive words of Thomas Chalmers, " We have no experience in the creation of worlds." Such speculations are quite as useless as materialistic efforts to account for the origin of life on our globe. No matter how much we seek to dignify our fancies with imposing titles, and no matter how many names of illustrious scientists

may seemingly support one or another cosmic speculation, they are always at best but childish fancies and
have absolutely no scientific value. If the philosophic
conception of creation be sound, we can never by
studying the present-day behaviour of anything discover the method of its origin.

II

And we are driven to this identical conclusion when
we begin to study the problem of the origin of the
chemical elements. The new science of radioactivity,
with the many studies in physical chemistry which
have developed under its inspiration, has shown that
there is a real gamut of the elements, running from
the lowest or lightest, hydrogen, up to the heaviest,
uranium, which becomes number 92 of the series.
Whether or not helium can be supposed to be built up
of four hydrogen atoms, and the other elements also
be built up in a similar way, is merely a matter of
speculation. Science knows nothing whatever of any
such synthetic composition or evolution of the elements. But in contrast we do know definitely of the
disintegration of the elements. Certain elements of
high atomic weight are constantly breaking up into
other elements of lower atomic weight, this disintegration being caused by the atoms of the heavy element
steadily and inevitably breaking up and losing some
of their component parts. All atoms are now known
to be composed of a certain number each of electrons
and protons; and when an element loses one or more
of these from one of its atoms, the remainder of this
atom which is left behind has become one of the other
elements lower down in the series. Uranium by its
disintegration is changed into radium, and the latter

after undergoing several more changes becomes one of the isotopes of lead.

We have not yet been able to detect all of the elements in this process of disintegration; but we have observed it in the case of several, and we infer that the same thing holds true of the others. Furthermore, no amount of heat or chemical manipulation serves to hasten this process of the disruption or disintegration of the atoms; and on the other hand no cold or other precaution seems to have the slightest effect in slowing up the process. This breaking up of the atoms of high atomic weight into other atoms of lower atomic weight, seems to be a fundamental tendency of the stuff which we call matter. And we have absolutely no knowledge whatever that the reverse process is anywhere going on throughout the universe, in spite of Prof. R. A. Millikan's courageous speculation that somewhere, away off in the laboratories of the stars, this reverse process may be now going on.[1] (*The Significance of Radium, Science,* July 1, 1921.)

Thus we have reached the conception of the universe as being composed of over seven dozen kinds of

[1] Note.—Sir Oliver Lodge seems to have caught the same idea, and is trying to Coué himself into believing that somewhere in the remote corners of the universe this building up of the elements is going on. He says: "But we have not learned how to pack hydrogen into helium or into any other of the heavier atoms—as yet. No, not yet. And yet it would appear that it must have been done, some time and somewhere; perhaps in the interior of stars, certainly in ways at present unknown." (*Scientific American,* May, 1924.) Similarly some mechanic might say that he had not yet learned the trick of perpetual motion; or some belated follower of Charlton Bastian might say that he had not yet been able to demonstrate spontaneous generation—as yet; no, not yet.

elements which are like so many clocks all running down, with no means known to science of their being wound up again.   From this it follows that these chemical elements cannot possibly have existed as they are from all eternity; for with an infinity of past existence they must all have been disintegrated long ago, or must long ago have run down.   Thus we reach the conviction that, so far as modern science gives us any information whatever, these elements, which are the bricks of which the material universe is composed, must at some definite time in the past have been created.   It makes no matter how long ago its creation took place; it must have been a real creation, and the period of time since it took place must be of definitely limited duration.   Matter certainly is not eternal; it must have been created by God.

III

We reach the same conclusion when we deal with the living things now existing on our globe.   Science knows nothing of the theory of spontaneous generation, except that this theory has been wholly discredited by every suitable experiment during the last five decades. Life comes now only from antecedent life of a similar kind; and we know nothing that offers any promise of showing us how in our day the living can possibly arise from the not-living.   In other words, spontaneous generation can no longer be dignified with the title of being a scientific theory; it is quite unscientific; and Harvey's dictum of *Omne vivum ex ovo,* has for many decades been victorious all along the line.

This means that life in some form must have been created by God Himself.   When Charles Schuchert, in speaking of this problem of the origin of life, says that "it is the greatest of the unsolved problems confronting man," he only shows that as a materialistic philosopher he refuses to accept the plain and obvious teaching of modern science which would immediately solve this problem in the only possible way. I am not a materialist, and I am not ashamed to mention the name of God or the term "creation" in connection with scientific explanations. Why should men balk like stubborn mules, when confronted with this question of the origin of life, and persist in saying that it is the greatest of all problems still remaining unsolved by modern science? Surely, if there is one problem that has been solved by modern science it is this regarding the origin of living matter: *it must have been created in the beginning*. There is no other explanation of the origin of life which deserves a moment's consideration in this third decade of the twentieth century. The only rational theory to-day regarding the origin of life is that God created it.

But right here we need to reason very carefully. There is no such thing as life in the abstract. That is, life is not an entity. It has no existence apart from concrete living substances or organisms. Accordingly, it must have been one or more of these organisms which God originally created in the beginning. Which of these was it? Are we to suppose that He made one little speck of protoplasm, such as one of the protozoa or a unicellular plant? How long, do you think, such a lonely little organism could exist? Only long enough to starve to death, unless there were innumerable other organisms accompanying it. This notion of life having originated in the form of unicellular organisms has been put forth by some who have not taken the trouble to think the matter out in detail; but it is in reality one of the most silly and childish theories with which I am acquainted. Its proponents seem never to take into account the fact that the living world as we know it, which is the only world of which we have any experimental knowledge whatever, *is a balanced world, an interdependent world;* and it is impossible to conceive of the lower forms of life, even a multitude of them, as existing in the world without the existence also of the complementary forms of life which we call the higher organisms. I utterly refuse to believe that the unicellular animals and plants could exist for a week without many accompanying higher forms; and I also deny the possibility of these higher forms existing for any great length of time without great multitudes of the so-called lower forms. The organic world as we have come to know it is a balanced and orderly world; and as far as we can judge its component parts are each essential for the welfare of all the other parts.

What then was it that must have been created in the beginning? Some organisms must have been called into existence in a way different from any process that we now call a natural process. As I have pointed out in a former book (*Q. E. D., or New Light on the Doctrine of Creation;* 1917), the essential idea of creation, as taught in the Bible, is that matter, and life, and the various distinct kinds of life, must have been brought into existence at some time in the past through a process wholly different, both in the degree and the kind of power exerted, from any process now going on around us which we call a natural process. The essence of the evolution doctrine is that only these modern natural processes have prevailed during all past time; the present is the measure of the past and the measure of all the past. But creation is the exact antithesis of this. It teaches that things originated in the past by some method quite distinct from those natural laws which are now being displayed in perpetuating them. And we now see that so far as matter or life is concerned, they call for a real creation at the beginning, and negative the theory of evolution here at the very threshold of our investigation.

IV

But again I ask, What kinds of life must have been created at the beginning?

Zoologists have divided the animals into a certain number of *phyla* or groups. The number of these phyla vary with different scientists from eight to eleven or more. Each phylum is divided into *classes;* the phylum Chordata, which includes the vertebrates, being divided into the amphibia, reptilia, mammalia and various others. But each class is again divided into *orders;* the mammalia being divided into the carnivora, rodentia, the proboscidea, the primates, and many others. The orders are further subdivided into *families,* the families into *genera,* and the genera into *species.*

Of course, in any system of clear thinking, we must understand that these phyla and classes and orders and families, and even the genera and species, *are mere abstractions;* they have no existence whatever except as we imagine a number of individual organisms to be grouped together and separated from all other animals so as to make one of these collections. *The things that really do exist are the individual organisms.* And it is obvious that in any system of evolution we must start with some lowly or " generalized " forms which we may think are sufficiently inclusive to permit of the other or more highly specialized types being developed from them. In other words, we cannot start with a phylum, and evolve a class from it, and from the latter evolve an order and a family; for these are all abstractions. What we must do, in any system of evolution, is to start with some such forms as the protozoa, and then try to imagine how the porifera, or sponges, have been developed from them. But the porifera will never do as the source or origin of the coelenterates, nor will the latter serve to originate the echinoderms, the arthropods, or the mollusks. In other words, all of these phyla are so distinct from one another that no stretch of the imagination will permit us to suppose that any one phylum has been developed from any other phylum as now existing.

But the very same principle holds good with regard to the *classes* or even the *orders*. For instance, we have no scientific knowledge of how the vertebrates could have originated from any non-vertebrated types. Evolutionists are fond of asserting that the class *Aves* (birds) have somehow originated from the dinosaurs, or at least from some reptilian ancestors. But this is wholly incredible and without a shred of scientific evidence in its support.

Similarly I deny that there is any scientific evidence to show that the placental mammals have sprung from the marsupials or the monotremes. Also I deny that there is any scientific evidence to show that such orders as the carnivora or the insectivora have sprung from some common " generalized " ancestor. Furthermore, I do not believe that the various families included in any given order have originated from any common ancestor. For instance, there are some twenty-two species of dogs found in North America, which are included under the family of the Canidae; some twelve species of bears included under the family of the Ursidae; also some eight species of cats included under the Felidae. All of these and many other families are included under the order Carnivora.

Now, I am willing to grant that all of the cats over the world may have had a common origin; that all of the bears may have had a common origin; or that all of the genera included under the Canidae may have had a common origin. Yet I utterly deny that there is any scientific evidence worthy of the name to intimate that the cats and the bears and the dogs have all sprung from a common more generalized type in the long ago. Of organic evolution in this sense of the term there is not a shred of evidence worthy of being called scientific.

Thus we have reached the crux of our whole argument. Charles Darwin entitled his great work *The Origin of Species;* and he and most of his successors have assumed that when they have proved the derivation of several species from a common generic type, they have thereby demonstrated the truth of organic evolution. In previous chapters I have pointed out the high probability that many modern species have had a common origin in the not very remote past. Indeed, it would seem probable that not only many Jordanian " species," but even many Linnaean species, have originated through natural causes since the original creation. I believe this fully. It is even quite possible that in some cases at least all of the genera under a family may have thus been " evolved," if the reader wishes to use this term, from some common original stock. But to call this process " evolution " is a confusion of terms.

In this connection, I consider the views set forth by Dr. H. B. Guppy, about 1906, and afterwards adopted and advocated by Dr. J. C. Willis and others, are not very far from the truth. Willis states the theory as follows, namely, " that evolution did not proceed from individual to variety, from variety to species, from species to genus, and from genus to family, but inversely; the great families and genera appearing at a very early period, and subsequently breaking up into other genera and species " (*Age and Area,* p. 221; 1922. Cambridge University Press.)

Guppy's theory involves the thought that the great family types must have originated in the long ago by some process quite different from those processes which have since split these family types up into genera and species. To quote his own words: " The age that witnessed the rise of the great families and the age that witnessed their subsequent differentiation are things apart, and cannot be dealt with by the same method " (Linnaean Society's *Journal,* Vol. XLIV, p. 457; 1919). He does not expressly say that these family types must have been created, *de novo;* but I do not see what other alternative there can be. Because, to quote the words of Prof. D. H. Scott, which he uses in connection with this theory of Guppy's about the origin of the great families of the angiosperms, " We know nothing whatever of the origin of the angiospermous families " (*Extinct Plants and Problems of Evolution,* p. 217; 1924). That is, we do not know any more about the origin of these great family types than we do about the origin of life itself. And who is there to-day with an adequate scientific training that will have the hardihood to defend the theory of spontaneous generation?

In the light of what these leading botanists are now telling us, I can see nothing left of the theory of organic evolution as a whole. And if the zoologists would only learn the lesson that the botanists seem to have learned, I think that we would all be not far from the kingdom.

Regarding the ancestral forms of the great families of both animals and plants, I can see nothing but a direct creation by the great Author of nature. Anything less than this I call speculation and pseudoscience. It seems to me that the creation of at least the families, and in some cases the genera, is the only hypothesis that in this year of grace, 1924, we can call scientific and reasonable. Furthermore, from the facts of geology as we now know them, *we may well believe that all these great ancestral types may have been created together, and that they long lived contemporaneously together, until many of them were destroyed in the great world cataclysm.* Because there is no adequate evidence, capable of critical examination, which will prove that the invertebrates existed before the vertebrates, that the fishes lived before the reptiles, or the latter before the birds and mammals. Or to be specific, there is no adequate evidence that the dinosaurs lived before the elephants, or that the trilobites lived before the ammonites or the dinosaurs.

V

If now we turn to man and his nearest allies, the anthropoid apes, we find that the latter are placed in the Simiidae, with four genera, the gibbons, the orangutans, the gorillas, and the chimpanzees; while the former is in a family by himself, the Hominidae, being designated as *Homo sapiens.*

The physical resemblances between man and the anthropoid apes have been often recounted, but need not detain us here. These resemblances are admittedly considerable. Contrastedly, however, is the vast difference in the mental faculties, not to mention man's moral and spiritual capacity of communing with and obeying his Creator.

Many arguments have been adduced to prove that man is a developed ape; yet not a single one of these arguments but would just as logically prove that the apes are degenerate or hybrid men. There are no clear and positive evidences from paleontology which would prove that the existing anthropoid apes existed before the great world cataclysm, or the Deluge. These present-day anthropoid apes may be just as much a product of modern conditions as are the negroid or the Mongolian types of mankind. And if I were compelled to choose between saying that the apes are degenerate or hybridized men and that man is a developed ape, I am sure it would not take me very long to decide which it would be. Nor do I think it ought to take any well-informed scientist long to make the choice.

If we compare the modern elephants, or bears, or elks, or indeed any single type of mammal, with their fossil types of the Pleistocene, we see in every single case a degeneration. Similarly, when we compare the best of the modern races of men *physically* with the Cro-Magnards of the deposits of Western Europe, we also see a degeneracy, although we cannot be sure that these Cro-Magnard men, the finest race the world has ever seen, as Macnamara says, were really antediluvian. Accordingly, by every just rule of comparison and analogy, we may well declare that if there is any blood relationship between man and the anthropoid apes, it is the latter which have degenerated from the former, instead of the former having developed from the latter. I do not say that this is the true solution of this enigma; but I do say that *there is far more scientific evidence in favour of this hypothesis* than there ever has been in favour of the long popular theory that man is a developed animal.

There can be but one conclusion for every man in our day who will take the trouble to inform himself fully regarding all the scientific facts now available. *Man was created, he has not evolved.* By every known analogy, as we compare our modern mammals with the magnificent specimens of animal life which lie buried in the Pleistocene and Tertiary strata, yes, even in the Mesozoic beds, we may conclude that man originally was probably larger and of a more commanding physique than at present. Probably we have not yet recovered any specimens of true antediluvian man. Certainly such examples as the Neanderthal skull-cap, the Heidelberg jaw, or the Piltdown skull, are not of this character; nor is there any good geological or other evidence to prove that these specimens are very ancient, that is, that they were truly contemporary with those semitropical mammals which roamed over Western Europe in those primal days of perpetual spring when the world was young. Whether we shall or shall not at some future day recover some true specimens of that antediluvian race, is merely a matter of conjecture, or of hope. But certain it is that all the scientific evidence now available points to the fact that *man was originally created on a higher plane structurally and anatomically than he is at present.* In this respect also, modern science is confirming that record in the early chapters of **Genesis**, that man was created " in the image of God."

VI

In concluding this series of studies in regard to the origin of things, we must say that organic evolution, as commonly taught by scientists, is truly a phantom; it cannot be a true account of the method by which the plants and animals of our modern world have come to be what they are. All of those arguments under the influence of which it came into existence and gained popular acceptance, are now seen to have been fallacious. We have been reviewing these arguments in the foregoing pages. But the overwhelming evidence against the entire idea of evolution, and in favour of the opposite doctrine of a real creation, can be appreciated only by looking at these subjects in a broad way, and by including in our survey some things which are somewhat outside the field of biology proper.

The facts now known to modern science which have a bearing upon this problem of creation versus evolution, may be summarized as follows, the reader being referred to my special treatise on this subject for the more minute details.

1. *Matter must have been created*. It is not merely that we know nothing of the evolution of matter. Radioactivity proves that *matter is disintegrating, not evolving*. The ninety-two elements may be spoken of as just so many clocks now running down, with no known method of winding them up. Hence, they could not have existed in this condition during an infinite past time: they must have had a beginning. And the only adequate beginning which we can conceive of is a real creation by a living and eternal God.

Matter is not eternal; it must have had a beginning, that is, it must have been created.

2. *Life must have been created.* And this must have included *many diversified forms of life,* at least; for it is quite inconceivable that one little speck of protoplasm, such as a protozoon or a bacterium, could have lived and persisted, even if it had been created alone in the world. Just how much of a community of living things would be essential for the perpetuity of the whole, by providing for the interdependence of the various kinds of life, we do not know. But the web of life is so intricate, and withal so inexorable in its demands and conditions, that there is little doubt that several representatives at least of each of the phyla would be essential to the welfare of the whole, perhaps even essential to their sheer existence. And of course, the various animal forms could not exist without the complementary plants; for the latter are indispensable in preparing the inorganic elements as food for the animals, by means of photosynthesis. It may be questioned whether the existence of the higher vertebrates and of the higher orders of plants would be essential to the existence of the lower forms; probably our replies to such a question would always be a mere matter of opinion. But it is scientifically certain that a mere few of the lower forms of life could not exist very long alone on our earth, without a continuous miracle being performed to keep them alive.

3. *It is incredible that the members of any single phylum could have developed out of the members of any other phylum; and also quite as incredible that any two phyla could have developed from any common original.* This generalization seems so self-evident that it need not be discussed further.

4. But it seems to me that the very same generalization can be *extended to the classes, the divisions, and the orders*. As we are here dealing only with the animal kingdom, we may illustrate the last of these divisions, the *orders,* by such types as the Edentata, the Ungulata, the Carnivora, or the Primates. It is quite inconceivable that any of the orders could have been derived from any others, or that any two of them could have had a common origin by any methods of variation and heredity now known to us. I say, " now *known* to us;" for if we permit ourselves to indulge in pure speculations, there is no halting until we reach the fantasies of *Alice in Wonderland* or of *The Wizard of Oz.*

5. It seems to me that the very largest group which we can scientifically conceive of having all descended from a common original pair (and it *needs a pair* in every instance of the higher types), is the *Family.* I concede that it is believable that all the members of each of such families as the Felidae (cats), the Canidae (dogs, wolves, etc.), the Suidae (pigs), or the Equidae (horses), could be of a common origin, though I think that in some cases we ought to descend to the *genus.* This uncertainty, however, is due to our methods of taxonomy. There is some unit of classification larger than a " species " as now commonly understood, and usually larger than the genus, which must nevertheless serve as the largest unit which our scientific knowledge permits us to postulate as the group which now represents all the forms or kinds which have probably descended from some common original pair. Linnaeus had this same idea; only he called his unit the " species." Subsequent discoveries in biology have done two things for this concept; they

have degraded the term " species " by pushing it down the scale to what Linnaeus wished to call varieties; and they have also shown that much more variation is possible within the limits of the " species " than Linnaeus would allow.   Hence, the term " species " is now utterly spoiled for the concept for which Linnaeus intended it.   In the light of modern knowledge, we may now use the term " Family " in the original sense in which Linnaeus used the term " species," when he said: *Species tot sunt diversae quot diversae formae ab initio sunt creatae,*—thus making the number of species correspond to the number of kinds created in the beginning.   To-day this dictum is absolutely true, if we substitute the word *familia* for the word *species*.

VII

The geological theory of a succession of life-forms, has long been supposed to forbid any such view of a real creation of all the leading types of life at some one time in the past.   That is, geology has been supposed to prove that the various types of life have come into existence a few at a time, in a long series which has been supposed to have been truly chronological. But we now know that this is all a mistake.   We now know that the Cambrian fossils are not intrinsically older than the Cretaceous or the Tertiary.   To give but two examples, in Montana we know that the Cretaceous fossils were deposited *before* the Cambrian and various other Paleozoic types, while in the Salt Range of India, the Tertiary forms were laid down *before* the Cambrian of that particular locality. In other words, we now know that these geological formations merely *represent ancient floras and faunas* buried near to their former habitats; and the geological series does not represent a chronology any more than would a similar serial arrangement of the floras and faunas of the modern world.

This new knowledge from geology makes it easy for us to say that there *could* have been a real creation of all the leading types of life at some one definite time in the long ago. And now biology, in spite of Darwinism,—nay, even because of the studies inspired by the theory of organic evolution,—is telling us that we cannot understand how any of these leading representative types could have originated, except by a real creation.

Also our modern knowledge regarding the possibilities of variation is now clearing up a very important difficulty. For when the idea of Cuvier prevailed regarding the " fixity " of species, it was indeed a very great difficulty to account in a reasonable way for the many kinds of plants and animals which were salvaged from the ruins of the antediluvian world. A great deal of amusement has been extracted by scoffers from the account given in Genesis concerning the animals which were preserved in Noah's ark. This difficulty would indeed be a real one if we had to suppose that samples of all the present " species " of animals were thus preserved in the ark. But in the light of what we now know about the possibilities of variation, as brought out by modern experiments in breeding, this difficulty is enormously reduced. Just what the conditions of the problem would really be, in the light of the modern discoveries, it might be difficult to state; but at any rate this problem is not such a tremendous one as it once appeared to such men as Linnaeus, or Owen, or Agassiz, who believed the old ideas about the " fixity " of species. Charles Darwin had been brought up under these old ideas regarding the " fixity " of species, and his life-work was devoted to showing that " species " are not thus fixed, or wholly incapable of change. The vast amount of facts which Darwin brought forward proved very convincing to the scientific world. He seemed to prove his case completely. And subsequent investigations have confirmed this part of what Darwin taught. Mendelism has now come in to supplement and clarify our knowledge regarding the precise ways in which plants and animals tend to vary. But all of the facts which have thus been accumulated are now seen to be only so many means of assisting us to understand how the great diversity among the plants and animals of our modern world may have come about from comparatively few originals which survived from the great world catastrophe of the Deluge.

VIII

Thus we find ourselves back again to that point which we have already visited so many times in these studies, namely, to the idea that geology holds the master key to this entire problem of the origin of living things. In the light of all our modern knowledge, it is evident that the theory of organic evolution has but a very slender support in biology. Without a strongly contributory geological background, nobody would ever dream of a scheme of organic evolution. If geology cannot prove in the most positive and conclusive manner that the Paleozoic animals and plants actually lived and died before the Mesozoic and the Tertiary ones came into existence, what is the use of talking about a theory of organic evolution? What method of origin for our modern plants and animals could we imagine, except a real creation of their representative ancestors at some definite period in the long remote past?

We may expect that there will always be those who will continue to speculate regarding the origin of things, just as there is still an annual crop of people who persist in fooling away their time with such matters as perpetual motion or spontaneous generation. We cannot hope that the world will ever be free from such vagaries. But the time is coming when such puerilities will no longer be put before the world in the name of venerable institutions of learning, under the imprimatur of respectable publishing houses, and under the aegis of the sacred name of natural science.

Here we must rest our argument. If the geological series does not represent a real chronology, but merely various contemporary faunas and floras; in other words, if the alleged chronology of the fossils is merely a big blunder, or at best an evolutionary assumption, the way is open for every intelligent person to believe in a literal creation of all the leading types of life, man included, as recorded in the first chapters of the Bible.

This is the latest and most authoritative word of modern science regarding the oldest and most fundamental problem of religion.

BIBLIOGRAPHY

Bateson, Wm., *Evolutionary Faith and Modern Doubts; Science,* January 20, 1922.

Bower, F. O., *The Present Outlook on Descent; Nature,* March 8, 1924.

Dennert, E., *At the Deathbed of Darwinism;* 1904.

Fairhurst, A., *Organic Evolution Considered;* 1913.

Jeans, J. H., *The Origin of the Solar System; Nature,* March 1, 1924.

Lock, R. H., *Variation, Heredity, and Evolution;* 1920.

Morgan, T. H., *A Critique of the Theory of Evolution;* 1916.

Price, G. McC., *The Fundamentals of Geology;* 1913.

        Q. E. D., or New Light on the Doctrine of Creation; 1917.

        The New Geology; 1923.

Scott, D. H., *The Present Position of the Theory of Descent; Nature,* September 29, 1921.

        Extinct Plants and Problems of Evolution; 1924.

Shapley, Harlow, *Address Before the Brit. Astron. Ass'n; Nature,* 21, 28, 1922.

Soddy, F., *The Interpretation of Radium;* 1920.

Willis, J. C. (and others), *Age and Area;* 1922.

ROBERT E. SPEER

Seeking the Mind of Christ $1.50

"Filled with the very soul of scriptural teaching most deeply spiritual and vital in every outreach; a book of sound doctrine. Dr. Speer's well-known staunchness and virility in Christian faith will be appreciated at once. Familiarity with this volume should put iron in the blood of Christian thinking, boldness in Christian aspiration, and meaning in Christian service."—*Christian Evangelist.*

WILLIAM MELVILLE CURRY, D.D.

Pastor, Ninth Presbyterian Church, Philadelphia

The Pastor's Corner

An Intimate Discussion of Moral and Spiritual Problems. Introduction by Charles R. Erdman, D.D.
$1.50

This group of brief and vivid messages from a pastor to his people, printed week by week in the Calendar of the Ninth Presbyterian Church, Philadelphia, is marked by spiritual insight, practical wisdom, quiet humor and broad knowledge of the multitudinous aspects of human life.

JOHN ELLIOTT WISHART, D.D., LL.D.

San Francisco Theological Seminary

The Fact of Prayer

Its Problems and Possibilities. Introduction by Prof. Melvin G. Kyle, D.D. $1.75

Clear and convincing, this work provides a solid foundation for Christian belief in the value and valdity of prayer between man and God. This book is one for both scholar and layman—it satisfies both mind and heart.

WILLIAM CARTER, Ph.D., D.D.

The Other Side of the Door

With Introduction by S. Parkes Cadman, D.D., President, Federal Council of Churches. $1.50

A distinctly novel note is struck by Dr. Carter in these fourteen sermons. Here are addresses on youth, maturity, womanhood, and specifically on redemption of the soul and the life in Christ Jesus. There are such striking titles as "Milestones on the Way to God," "Tadmar in the Wilderness," "The Pillars of the Earth," and "A Chance for Every One."

F. G. FROST, M.A. (Compiler)

The Message of F. W. Robertson

An Anthology of Pulpit Masterpieces. Introduction by R. J. Campbell, D.D. $1.25

Six hundred brief, pithy and invigorating extracts from Dr. Robertson's effective sermons, each excerpt being directly applicable to the life of to-day. The titles and the index increase the book's value to ministers and other Christian workers. An extremely helpful and inspiring volume for stimulating devotional reading.